CB030963

ACTIVITY BOOK B

MACMILLAN

Carol Read • Mark Ormerod

Macmillan Education
4 Crinan Street
London N1 9XW
A division of Macmillan Publishers Limited
Companies and representatives throughout the world

ISBN 978 0 230 47573 1

Text © Carol Read and Mark Ormerod 2013
Design and illustration © Macmillan Publishers Limited 2013

First published 2013

Extra material in the extension section by Rob Sved.

Designed by Carolyn Gibson
Illustrated by Lisa Althaus, Kevin Hopgood, Graham Howells,
Martin Impey, Nick Kobyluch, Andrew Painter, Pete Smith,
JHS Studios and Simon Walmesley
Cover design by Astwood Design Consultancy
Songs produced and arranged by Tom, Dick and Debbie
Productions
Recordings produced and arranged by RBA Productions
Pictures researched by Victoria Gaunt

Authors' acknowledgements

We would like to thank everyone at Macmillan Education in
the UK and in Spain who has helped us in the development
and the production of these materials. We would also like to
thank all the teachers who have taken time to read, pilot and
give feedback at every stage of writing the course. Special
thanks from Carol to Alan, Jamie and Hannah for their
encouragement and support. Special thanks from Mark to
Carlos for his patience and understanding.

Acknowledgements

The publishers would like to thank the following teachers:
Belén Lesma Ciruelos, CEIP María Pineda, Getafe, Madrid;
Eva Alsedà, Escola Gravi, Barcelona; Francesc Niella
Casas, Escola Montserratina, Viladecans, Barcelona; Maider
Etxebarria Garai, Leioa, Bizcaia; María Hernández Martí,
Escola Gitanjali, Badalona, Barcelona; María Verenciano
Benito, CEIP Nuestra Señora de las Latas, Loredo, Cantabria;
Mª Jesús Richart Company, Colegio San Juan y San Pablo,
Ibi, Alicante; Paco Sansaloni Felis, CEIP Cervantes, Gandía,
Valencia; Pere Truyols Carreras, CEIP Sant Bartomeu, Alaró,
Baleares; Rocío Galván Gallardo, CEIP Joaquín Benjumea
Burín, Sevilla; Silvia Sánchez Hernández, CEIP Pablo
Neruda, Alcalá de Henares; Sylvia Frei Salcedo, CEIP la
Cañada, Olías, Málaga.

Printed and bound in China

2018 2017 2016
12 11 10 9 8

The authors and publishers would like to thank the following
for permission to reproduce their photographs: **Alamy**/AF
archive p80(bl), Alamy/blickwinkel p78(b), Alamy/Nancy Hoyt
Belcher p76(bl), Alamy/Randy Duchaine p76(tm), Alamy/
Corbis Flirt p65(bl), Alamy/Moodboard p66(br), Alamy/patrick
nairne p64(bcl), Alamy/Sam Bloomberg-Rissman p64(tm),
Alamy/Alex Segre p64(bl); **Brand X Pictures** pp65(tr), 66(bcl);
Corbis p41(a), Corbis/Alan Copson/JAI p66(tcl), Corbis/
Laura Doss p9(br), Corbis/Antenna/fstop p65(br), Corbis/
Russell Glenister p50, Corbis/RobLewine p64(tl), Corbis/
Ocean p26(c), Corbis/Louie Psihoyos/Science Faction
p74(b), Corbis/Ragnar Schmuck/fstop p66(bcr), Corbis/
Gerhard Zwerger-Schoner/imagebroker p78(cr), CorbisKim
Walker/Robert Harding World Imagery p74(tr); **Fancy** p65(tl);
Getty Images pp64(tl,tr,br), 74(tl,tm), Getty Images/Monkey
Business Images p64(tcr), Getty Images/Martin Carlsson
p64(tcl), Getty Images/Laurence Cartwright Photography
p58, Getty Images/Federica Grassi p78(cl), Getty Images/
Glow Images, Inc p64(tr), Getty Images/Sean Justice p10(t),
Getty Images/Rob Lewine pp26(t), 28(t), Getty Images/Brand
X Pictures p34(cl), Getty Images/SSPL p41(c), Getty Images/
Simon Wilkinson p18; **Grapheast** p66(bcm);
Imagesource pp64(bcm,bcr), 65(tm), 66(tm), 66(bl), 78(tl);
Macmillan (statue) pp26, 28; **Photoshot**/WpN p76(tr);
Plainpicture/Maskot p10(c); **Rex Features** p41(b),
Rex Features/Monkey Business Images pp34(r,cr), Rex
Features/c.Universal/Everett p80(tr), Rex FeaturesAlastair
Muir p80(br), Rex Features/Ray Roberts p42(cr), Rex
Features/Image Source p9(tl); **Superstock**/Minden Pictures
p66(tcr), Superstock/Pixtal p76(br); **Thinkstock** p76(tl);
Wordsworth Editions p80(tl).

Stickers Alamy/Tetra Images, Alamy/Mark Mercer, Alamy/
Andrew Michael, Alamy/Mark Phillips, Alamy/Alex Segre,
Bananastock, Brand X pictures, Corbis, Corbis/Jon Boyes/
Spaces Images, Corbis/Richard Morrell, Corbis/Matthias
Ritzmann, Digital Vision, Getty, Getty Images/Debi Bishop,
Getty Images/Compassionate Eye Foundation/Drew Kelly,
Getty Images/Peter Muller, Getty Images/Chris Whitehead,
Imagesource, Macmillan, Rex Features/Ilpo Musto, Rex
Features/Stephanie Paschal, Stockbyte, Superstock/Robert
Harding/Loop Images.

Commissioned photography by Stuart Cox
pp3(tm,tr,cl,tr,cr), 4(tl,tmr,tml,tr), 6(tr,d,b,c,a), 9(tr),
36,39(cl,1,2,3,4), 40, 42(tl,tml,tmr,cl,cr),44,48, 50, 56.

Author photograph (Carol Read) by Michael Selley

Welcome Back to the Tiger Street Club!

Lesson 1 Vocabulary and Listening

1 Order and write.

1 new / got / a / T-shirt / I've

I've got a new T-shirt.

3 sports / I've / got / bag / a / new

_____

_____

2 We've / a / got / noticeboard / new

_____

_____

4 football / I've / got / new / a

_____

_____

2 Choose a card. CD1 Listen to the numbers. Play *Bingo!*

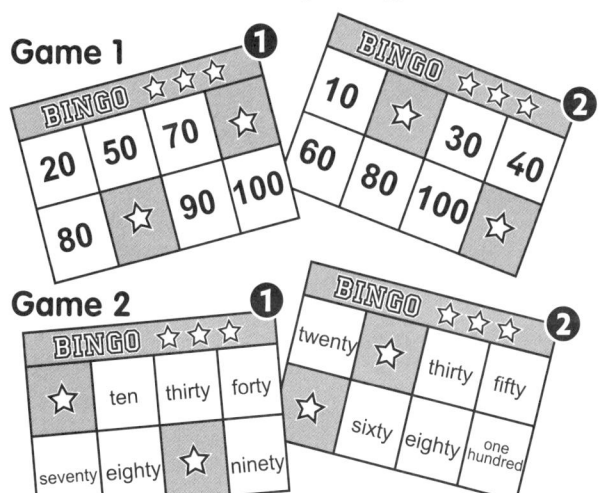

3 Look, read and write.

1 Number _thirty_ is on the cap.

2 Number _____ is on the computer.

3 Number _____ is on the chair.

4 Number _____ is on the sports bag.

5 Number _____ is on the football.

Lesson 2 Vocabulary

4 Write the months and complete the sentence.

```
¹M
²A      ³S          ⁴J
            ⁵J ⁶A
   ⁷N
   ⁸O
         ⁹J
      ¹⁰M
¹¹F
```

1 _____ 7 _____
2 _____ 8 _____
3 _____ 9 _____
4 _____ 10 _____
5 _____ 11 _____
6 _____

_____ is missing.

5 Write the questions and answers.

Nasim   Clare   Ben   Ellie

1 When is Nasim's birthday?   It's in October.
2 When is Clare's _____ ?   It's _____
3 _____ ?   _____
4 _____ ?   _____

January	February	March
		Clare's birthday
April	**May**	**June**
July	**August**	**September**
Ben's birthday		Start school
October	**November**	**December**
Nasim's birthday Ellie's birthday		

6 Write a name for every month. Ask your friends.

January	February	March
April	**May**	**June**
July	**August**	**September**
October	**November**	**December**

When's your birthday?

It's in … .

1 A New School Year

Lesson 1 Vocabulary

1 Find, circle and write.

MATHSSCIENCEHISTORY ENGLISH DRAMAPEGEOGRAPHYMUSICARTANDDESIGNICT

1 English   2 _____   3 _____   4 _____   5 _____

6 _____   7 _____   8 _____   9 _____   10 _____

2 Look. Write the first letter and find the sentence. Draw the time.

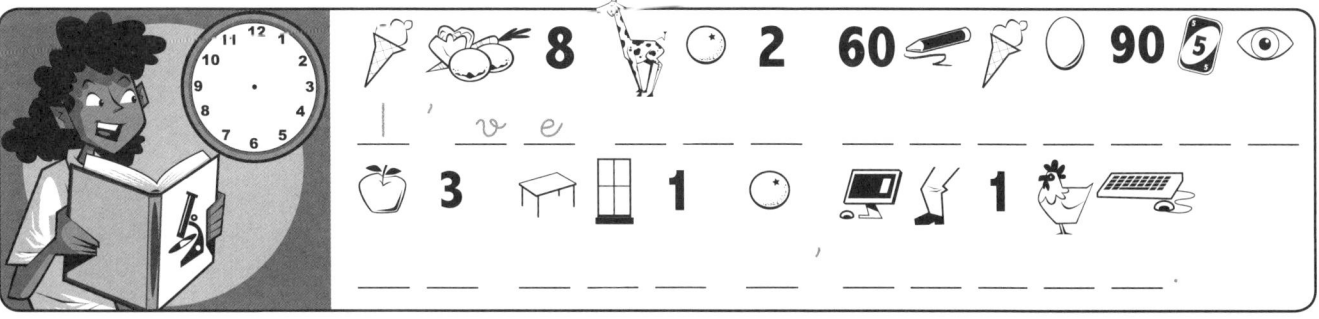

3 Look and write.

1 On Mondays, I've got art and design and science.
2 On Tuesdays, I've _____ and _____.
3 _____ and _____.
4 _____ and _____.
5 _____ and _____.

Morning	Timetable	Afternoon
Monday		
Tuesday		
Wednesday	10x15=150	
Thursday		
Friday	Hi Hello	

A New Friend

4 Read and number in order. CD1 15 Listen and check.

Oliver plays the recorder. ☐

Ellie plays the recorder, but it sounds terrible. ☐

Ellie says, 'This year, I want to learn to play a musical instrument.' ☐

It's the first day back at school. 1

They return the book and the recorder to Oliver. ☐

Ellie and Clare find a recorder and a music book. ☐

5 Order and write. Match. CD1 16 Listen and check.

1 half past nine / ? / What / we / have / at / got

What have we got at half past nine?

2 music / at / We've / quarter past ten / got

_____

3 play / recorder / the / want / to / I

_____

4 teach / I / you / can / play / to

_____

a

b

c

d

🏠 Home-School Link

6 me Read and reflect. Write. online materials

1 I think it _____ (is / isn't) very important to welcome new pupils on the first day of school.

2 I _____ (can / can't) play a musical instrument.

3 My favourite moment in the story is _____.

4 I think that Oliver is _____.

7 Write six words from the story. Tell your family what they mean.

1 _____ 2 _____ 3 _____

4 _____ 5 _____ 6 _____

Lesson 3 Grammar and Writing

8 Read and write. Learn.

We've got English (1) ___at___ quarter to ten.

We haven't (2) _____ science at quarter past nine.

Have we got PE today?   Yes, we (3) _____.

                   No, we (4) _____.

(5) _____ have we got at quarter past two?

We've got maths.

Tiger Tips

Remember!
- *we've got = we have got*
-

quarter   quarter
to   past

9 CD1 18   Listen, draw and write.

   1   It's _quarter past_ seven.

   2   It's _____ one.

   3   It's _____ five.

   4   It's _____ eight.

10 Look and write.

1   We haven't got PE at quarter past nine. We've got geography.

 9:15    X    ✓

2   We haven't got _____

    _____

10:45    X    ✓

3   Have we got English at quarter past twelve? Yes, we have.

12:15   Hi / Hello  ? ✓

4   _____

    _____

2:45    X   10 x 5 = 15 ✓

5   _____

    _____

3:45    ? X

11 Remember, write and say.

Fantastic phonics

we've got =
we have got

We've got

We've got

12 Look and write. **CD1 22** Listen and check. Act out.

1 What have we got at *quarter past ten* ?

2 We've got _____ . At _____ _____ , we've got _____ .

3 What have we got at _____ ?

4 We've got _____ . At _____ _____ , we've got _____ .

🏠 Home-School Link

13 Practise the dialogue at home with your family.

14 (me) Order and write. Tell your family what subjects you have got at different times of the day.

Wath   vahe   ew   ogt   ta   velnee   o'lckco?

W h a t _____ __ ___ __ _____ '____?

eW'ev   tog   lingsEh.

W e' __ ___ _____ .

Lesson 5 Reading, Writing and Grammar

15 → Go to Pupil's Book page 10. Look, read and write. Match.

Monday pupils ~~dance~~ centre
near classrooms Arts weekends

1 We have extra music, drama and ___*dance*___ classes.

2 I see my family at the _____.

3 All the pupils live _____ the school.

4 It's got 22 _____.

5 We go to Elm Park School in the _____ of London.

6 I live at the school from _____ to Friday.

7 Our school has got about 450 _____.

8 I go to Riverside School of Performing _____.

16 Order and write.

1 I / on / a / live / island / small
I live on a small island.

2 school / I / go / don't / to
_____

3 at / I / study / home / parents / with / my
_____

4 teacher / lessons / I / have / some / with / a _____

5 I / online / talk / to / children / other _____

17 Write sentences about your school.

My school has got _____
_____.

It hasn't got _____.

 **Culture • Project**

Lesson 6 Listening, Reading and Writing

18 **Listen and circle.**

Adam's school	big	small	very small
Start	9:00	9:15	9:30
Lunch	12:30	12:45	1:15
Finish	3:30	3:45	4:00
Favourite subjects	drama and history	music and maths	PE and ICT
After-school clubs			
Tuesdays	swimming club	science club	hockey club
Thursdays	board games club	sports club	art club

Adam

19 Read. CD1 27 **Listen and find the differences. Say stop.**

My notes:
- my school – small, London
- my timetable – begin: 9:30
  lunch: 1:15
  finish: 3:45
- my favourite subjects – geography, PE
- after-school clubs / activities – science, drama

Remember!
- 3:45 = quarter **to** four
- 4:15 = quarter **past** four

A day at school:
I go to a small school in the centre of London. Lessons begin at half past nine. We've got a break in the morning and in the afternoon. We have lunch at quarter past one. School finishes at quarter to four. My favourite subjects are geography and PE. On Mondays, I go to a science club. On Thursdays, I go to a drama club. I like drama.
by Ally

✏️ **Now write your notes and project in your notebook.**

🏠 **Home-School Link**

20 🖱️ **Use technology to extend your project.**

Lesson 7 Unit Review Vocabulary and Grammar

21 Look and write.

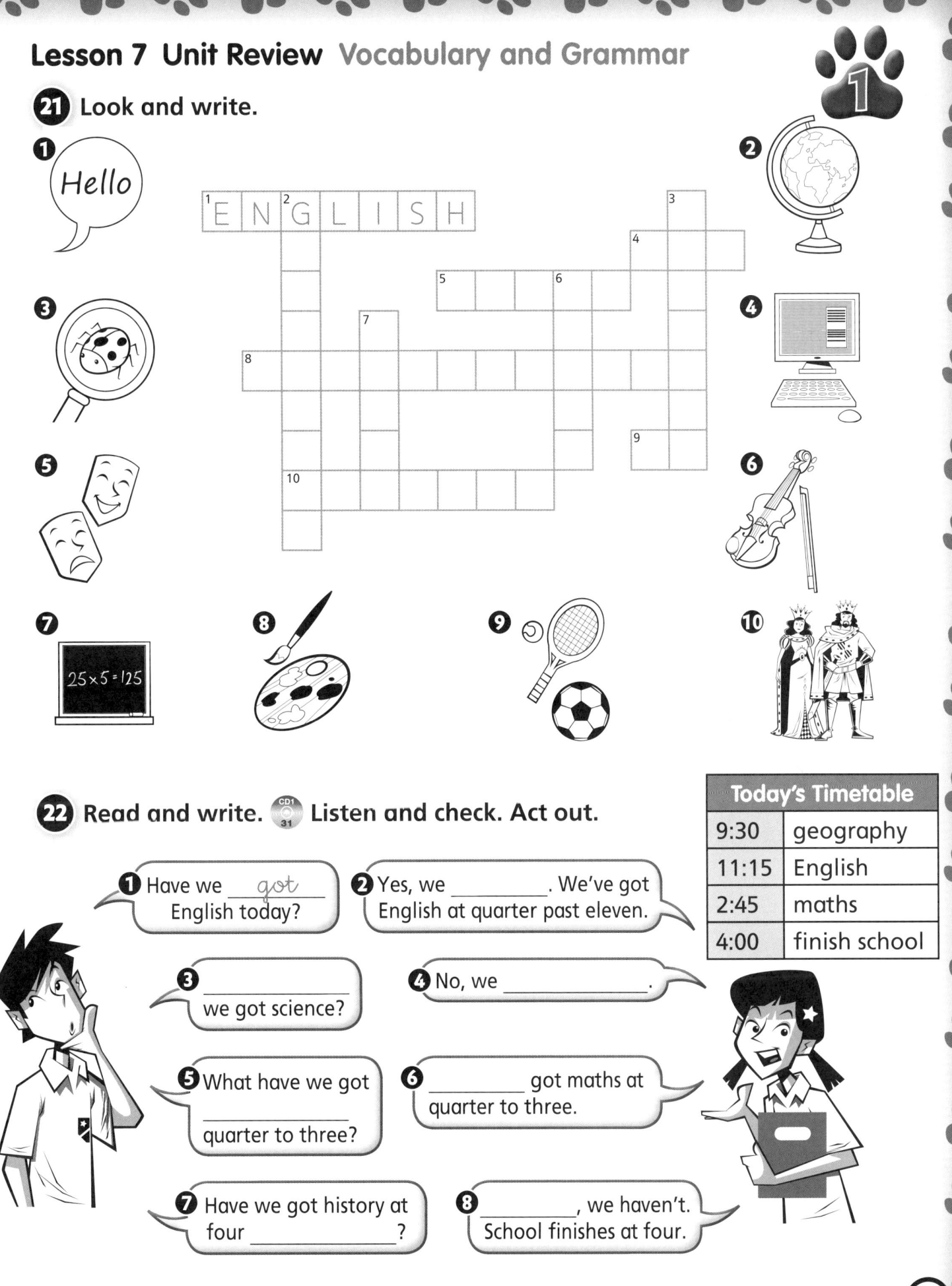

1 Hello

Crossword: 1 ¹E N ²G L I S H

22 Read and write. (CD1 31) Listen and check. Act out.

1 Have we ___got___ English today?

2 Yes, we _____. We've got English at quarter past eleven.

3 _____ we got science?

4 No, we _____.

5 What have we got _____ quarter to three?

6 _____ got maths at quarter to three.

7 Have we got history at four _____?

8 _____, we haven't. School finishes at four.

Today's Timetable	
9:30	geography
11:15	English
2:45	maths
4:00	finish school

Lesson 8 Unit Review CLIL, Culture and Self-assessment

23 **Read and predict.** CD1 32 **Listen and circle.**

I go to a very big school in (1) **London / Manchester**. The school has got about (2) **400 / 500** pupils. It's got 18 (3) **classrooms / gyms** and a canteen. It's got a big (4) **playground / canteen**.

I go to a performing arts school. I learn all the normal subjects, but I have extra (5) **music / science** lessons. I live at the school from Monday to (6) **Saturday / Friday**, but I see my family at the weekends.

24 **Order and write.**

1 very / I / to / small / go / school / a
   I go to a very small school.

2 to / On / drama / Mondays, / club / I / go
   _____

3 twelve / We / at / have / lunch / o'clock
   _____

4 subject / My / geography / favourite / is
   _____

25 CD1 33 **Listen and say *Yes* or *No*.**

26 **Complete the Picture Dictionary for Unit 1.**

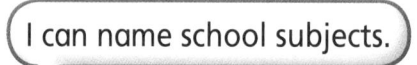
I can name school subjects.

🏠 Home-School Link

27 **Complete your *Tiger Team* score card.**

Yes.

Learning to **LEARN**

My Tiger Team score card

My work in Unit 1 is:		My Learning Plan
OK	☆	I plan to:
Good	☆☆	☐ read Unit 1 again
Very good	☆☆☆	☐ write a list of words to remember
Excellent	☆☆☆☆	☐ learn the grammar table
		☐ do the online activities

28 **Do an activity from your Learning Plan and complete your *Progress Journal* for Unit 1.**

2 Describing People

Lesson 1 Vocabulary

1 Look and write.

1 c*urly* h*air*

2 s*traight* h_____

3 b_____

4 m_____

5 l_____ h_____

6 s_____ h_____

7 g_____

8 p_____

9 f_____ h_____

10 d_____ h_____

2 Look. Write the first letter and find the sentence. Colour.

3 Look and write. Use the words.

1 *She's got long hair.*
(long)

2 *He's* _____
(glasses)

3 _____
(curly)

4 _____
(ponytail)

5 _____
(moustache)

6 _____
(short)

2 Lesson 2 A mystery

4 Read and write true sentences. CD1 38 **Listen and check.**

A Thief in the Park

1 Joe and Becky are in a park in Manchester.
Joe and Becky are in a park in London.

2 They see a woman take Peter Pan's flute.
_____

3 They call the hospital.
_____

4 The man has got the flute under his jumper.
_____

5 Look, read and write.

long got ~~coat~~ beard

1 The man is wearing a ____coat____.
2 He's got _____ dark hair.
3 He's _____ a moustache and a
   _____.

T-shirt hasn't moustache fair

4 The man is wearing a _____.
5 He's got short _____ hair.
6 He _____ got a beard or a
   _____.

🏠 Home-School Link

6 me Read and reflect. Write. online materials

1 *A Thief in the Park* is a _____ (fairy tale / mystery / legend).

2 I think the story is _____ (OK / good / very good / excellent).

3 My favourite moment in the story is _____.

4 I think it is important to tell an adult when you see someone
   _____ (suspicious / famous).

7 Write six words from the story. Tell your family what they mean.

1 _____   2 _____   3 _____
4 _____   5 _____   6 _____

Lesson 3 Grammar and Writing

Grrr... is for Grammar! 2

8 **Read and write. Learn.**

She's (1) ___got___ long fair hair.

She hasn't (2) _____ curly dark hair.

(3) _____ he got a beard?   Yes, he has.

Has he got a moustache?   No, he (4) _____ .

Tiger Tips
Remember!
- she's got = she has got
- No, he hasn't. = No, he has not.

9 **Look and write the letters.**

a I'm a clown.   **b** I'm a witch.   **c** I'm a dancer.   **d** I'm Father Christmas.

1 He hasn't got glasses. `d`   6 He's got curly dark hair. ☐

2 She hasn't got glasses. ☐   7 She's got fair hair. ☐

3 He's wearing a hat. ☐   8 He hasn't got a beard. ☐

4 She's got curly hair and glasses. ☐   9 He's got a beard and a moustache. ☐

5 She's wearing a hat. ☐   10 She's got a ponytail. ☐

10 **Look and write.**

1 The pirate _has got_ a ponytail and a beard.

2 He _____ glasses or a moustache.

3 He is _____ a hat.

4 The pop star _____ short fair hair.

5 She _____ a ponytail or glasses.

6 She is _____ a T-shirt.

11 Remember, write and say.

Fantastic Phonics

Where's _____

Here's _____

12 Read and tick (✓) the correct person. Write. *(CD1 43)* Listen and check.

1 **a** ☐ **b** ☐

Has he got fair hair? No, he hasn't.
Has he got glasses? Yes, he has.
Has he got a beard? _____

2 **a** ☐ **b** ☐

Has she got straight hair? No, she hasn't.
Has she got curly hair? Yes, she has.
Has she got glasses? _____

🏠 Home-School Link

13 Practise the questions and answers at home with your family.

14 Order and write. Act out.

1 Is / hat / ? / wearing / thief / a / the
<u>Is the thief wearing a hat?</u> Yes, she is.

2 long / Has / she / hair / ? / got
_____ Yes, she has.

3 hair / ? / got / Has / she / fair
_____ No, she hasn't.

4 Has / a / beard / ? / got / she
_____ Yes, she has, but it's a disguise.

5 Is / she / coat / ? / a / wearing
_____ Yes, she is.

15 Look and write.

> The Wizard of Oz   The Adventures of Sinbad
> ~~Alice's Adventures in Wonderland~~   Charlie and the Chocolate Factory

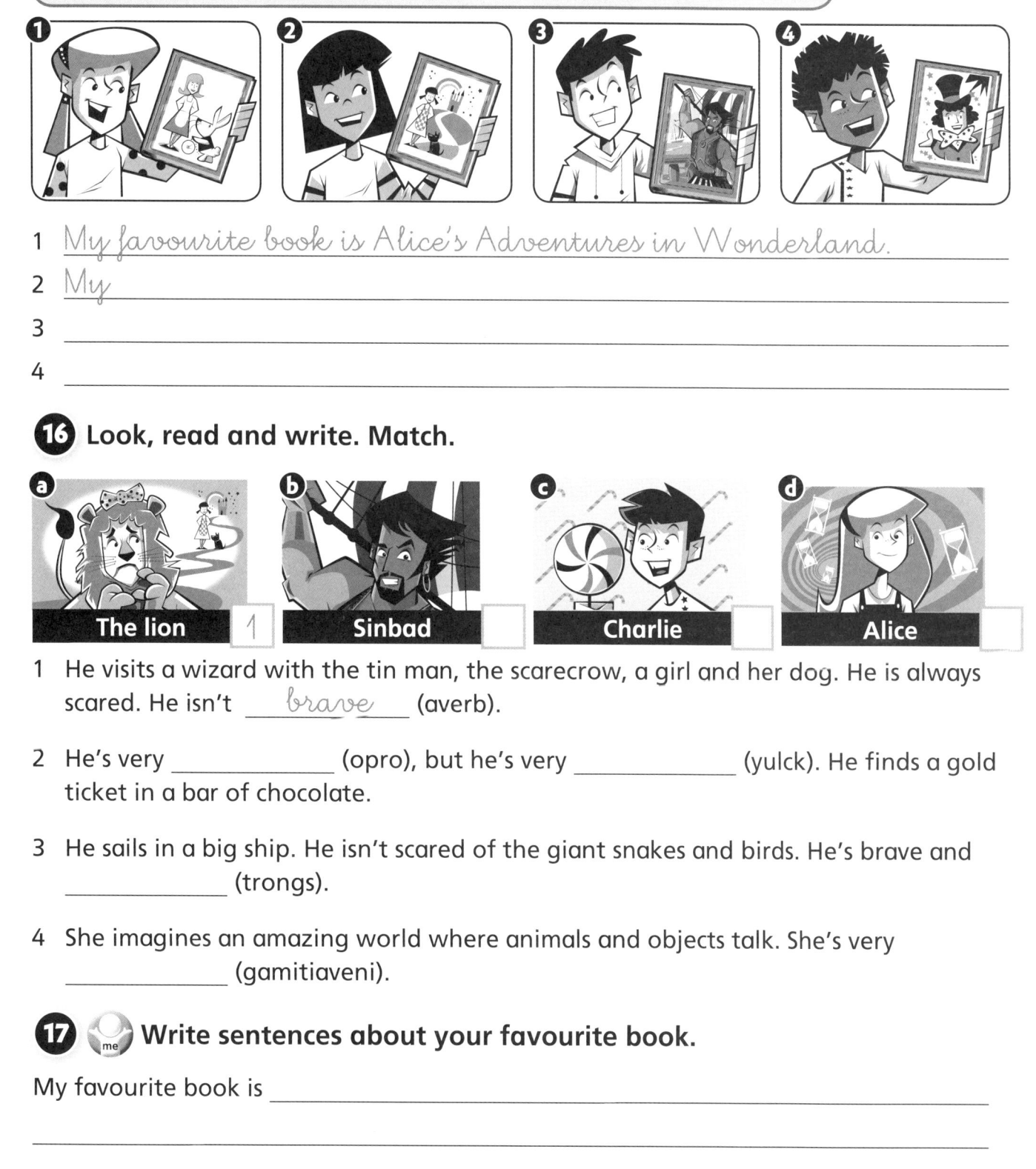

1 *My favourite book is Alice's Adventures in Wonderland.*
2 *My*
3 _____
4 _____

16 Look, read and write. Match.

The lion |1| Sinbad | | Charlie | | Alice | |

1 He visits a wizard with the tin man, the scarecrow, a girl and her dog. He is always scared. He isn't ___*brave*___ (averb).

2 He's very _____ (opro), but he's very _____ (yulck). He finds a gold ticket in a bar of chocolate.

3 He sails in a big ship. He isn't scared of the giant snakes and birds. He's brave and _____ (trongs).

4 She imagines an amazing world where animals and objects talk. She's very _____ (gamitiaveni).

17 me Write sentences about your favourite book.

My favourite book is _____

_____

_____.

Culture • Project

Lesson 6 Listening, Reading and Writing

18 **Listen and match.**

1

Anna

2

David

3

Sophie

4

Alex

a

b

c

d

19 **Read.** **Listen and find the differences. Say stop.**

My notes:

- title of the book — The Hundred and One Dalmatians
- the author — Dodie Smith
- the type of book — a children's novel
- my favourite character — Cruella de Vil
- a description of a character — beautiful, tall, black and white hair, fur coat, cruel

Remember!
- She's tall. = She **is** tall.
- She's got white hair. = She **has** got white hair.

My favourite book:

My favourite book is The Hundred and One Dalmatians, by Dodie Smith. The book is a children's novel. My favourite character is Cruella de Vil. Cruella is very beautiful. She's tall. She's got black and white hair. In the picture in my book, she's wearing a white fur coat. Cruella is very cruel.
by Sophie

 Now write your notes and project in your notebook.

 Home-School Link

20 **Use technology to extend your project.**

Lesson 7 Unit Review Vocabulary and Grammar

21 Look, read and write the words.

> ~~moustache~~ glasses beard ponytail curly hair
> straight hair dark hair fair hair short hair long hair

1 _moustache_

2

22 Read and write. *CD1 52* Listen and check. Act out.

1 Hello. There's a man in the library. I think he's a thief.

2 Can you describe him?

3 He's ___got___ long dark hair.

4 Has _____ got straight hair or curly hair?

5 He's got straight hair. _____ got a ponytail.

6 _____ he got a beard?

7 No, he _____. But he's got a moustache.

8 Has _____ got glasses?

9 Yes, he _____. And he's wearing a red hat and a green jumper.

Lesson 8 Unit Review CLIL, Culture and Self-assessment

23 Read and write. 🔊 CD1 53 Listen and check.

> lucky brave ~~clever~~ imaginative kind strong poor

1 The scarecrow and the tin man are from *The Wizard of Oz*. The scarecrow isn't _____clever_____. The tin man is very _____.

2 Sinbad is from *The Adventures of Sinbad*. He's _____ and _____.

3 Alice is from *Alice's Adventures in Wonderland*. She's very _____.

4 Charlie is from *Charlie and the Chocolate Factory*. He's _____, but he's very _____.

24 Order and write.

1 favourite / by / Hergé / book / My *Tintin in America* / is

My favourite book is Tintin in America by Hergé.

2 comic book / It / is / a

_____

3 character / My / is / Tintin / favourite

_____

4 hair / He's / got / fair

_____

5 brave / Tintin / very / is

_____

25 🔊 CD1 54 Listen and say *Yes* or *No*.

26 Complete the Picture Dictionary for Unit 2.

> I can name different types of hair.

> Yes.

Learning to **LEARN**

🏠 Home-School Link

27 Complete your *Tiger Team* score card.

My Tiger Team score card

My work in Unit 2 is:	My Learning Plan
OK ☆	I plan to:
Good ☆☆	☐ read Unit 2 again
Very good ☆☆☆	☐ write a list of words to remember
Excellent ☆☆☆☆	☐ learn the grammar table
	☐ do the online activities

28 Do an activity from your Learning Plan and complete your *Progress Journal* for Unit 2.

3 Around the Town

Lesson 1 Vocabulary

1 Look and write.

1 n*ewsagent's*

2 s_____

3 c_____

4 c_____

5 b_____ s_____

6 t_____ s_____

7 m_____

8 s_____

9 p_____ s_____

10 h_____

2 ♻ Look. Write the first letter and find the sentence.

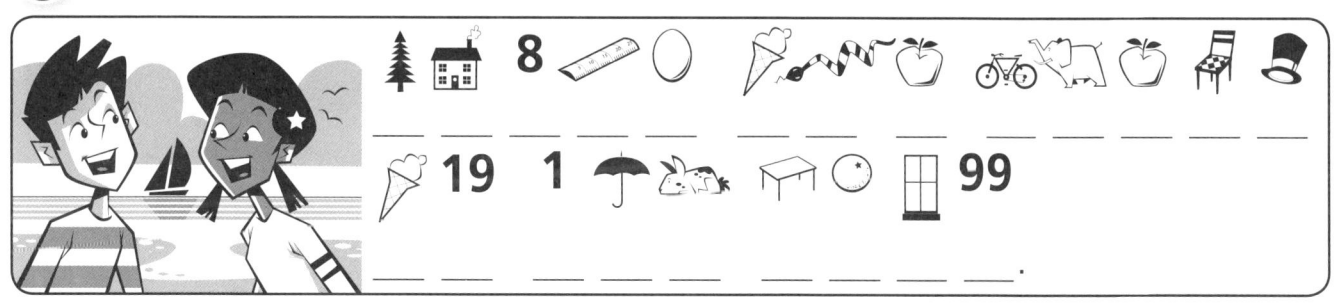

3 Look and write.

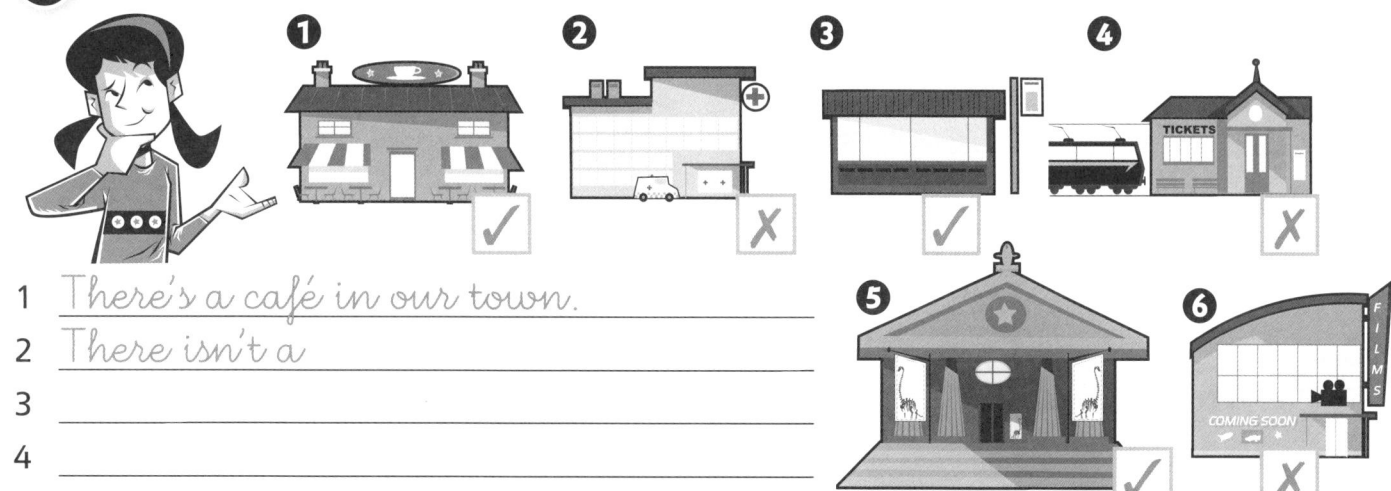

1 There's a café in our town.

2 There isn't a _____

3 _____

4 _____

5 _____

6 _____

3 Lesson 2 A fable

The Piper of Hamlin

4 Remember, complete and write *a* or *b*.

❶ I've got a magic _flute_, Mayor. I can make the rats go away. [b]

❷ I promise to give you this bag of _____. [ ]

❸ Are there any rats in _____ now? [ ]

❹ But sorry, I don't want to give you the _____. [ ]

❺ I want to teach the _____ a lesson. [ ]

❻ Thank you for making the _____ go away. [ ]

5 Write *There is* or *There are* and the correct prepositions.

1 _There are_ four rats ____in____ the car.

2 _____ three rats _____ the chair.

3 _____ two rats _____ the table.

4 _____ one rat _____ the door.

in   under   behind   on

🏠 Home-School Link

6 😊 Read and reflect. Write. online materials

1 I _____ (don't like / like / love) fables.

2 I think it _____ (is / isn't) very important to keep your promises.

3 My favourite moment in the story is _____.

4 I think the story is _____.

7 Write six words from the story. Tell your family what they mean.

1 _____   2 _____   3 _____

4 _____   5 _____   6 _____

Lesson 3 Grammar and Writing

Grrr... is for Grammar!

8 Read and write. Learn.

There (1) __'s__ a café in the street.

There (2) _____ houses in the street.

Is (3) _____ a supermarket?

(4) _____, there is.   (5) _____, there isn't.

(6) _____ there any shops?

Yes, (7) _____ are.   No, there (8) _____.

Tiger Tips
Remember!
- There's = There is
- There is ... + singular
- There are ... + plural

9 Look and write. Listen and check.

1 ___Is there___ a hospital in Cat Street?   ___No, there isn't.___

2 _____ a cinema in Cat Street?   _____

3 _____ two cinemas in Cat Street?   _____

4 _____ three bus stops in Cat Street?   _____

5 _____ a train station in Cat Street?   _____

6 _____ fourteen cats in Cat Street?   _____

10 Look, read and write.

in   under   on   ~~behind~~

1 Rat number 1 is ___behind the bus stop___.

2 Rat number 2 is _____.

3 Rat number 3 is _____.

4 Rat number 4 is _____.

11 Remember, write and say.

Fantastic Phonics

There's _____

There are _____

12 Order and write. CD2 12 Listen and check. Act out.

1 museum / Is / there / street / ? / a / your / in

Is there a museum in your street?

No, there isn't.

2 Are / any / shops / ? / there

_____

Yes, there are. There's a sweet shop and a pet shop.

3 any / your / street / ? / cinemas / Are / there / in

_____

No, there aren't.

4 a / Is / supermarket / ? / there

_____

Yes, there is. It's opposite the bus stop.

🏠 **Home-School Link**

13 Practise the dialogue at home with your family.

14 Read and write. Complete the sentence.

There's a café next to the police station.

There's a museum next to the café.

There's a supermarket opposite the police station.

There's a hospital next to the supermarket and the cinema.

The cinema is opposite the _____.

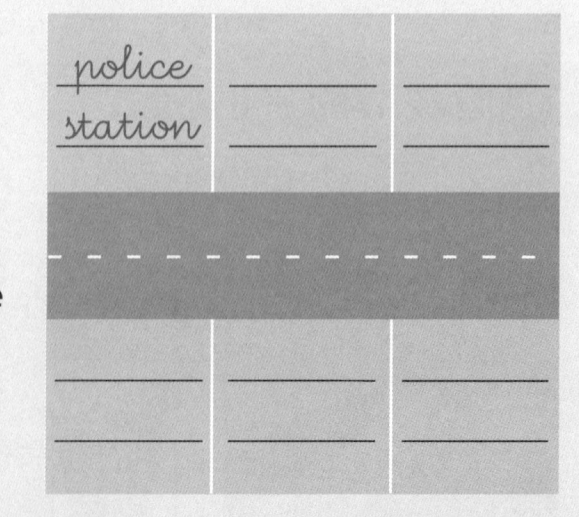

police station

Lesson 5 Reading, Writing and Grammar

15 Look and write.

```
        1               T
2           —           R
              3 T R A N S X I
4                        N
        5                S
                       6 P L A N E
              7          O
        8                R
                       9 T
```

16 Read and write true sentences.

1   In London, many people travel by double-decker taxi. Lots of people travel on the water bus.

_____

_____

2   In Venice, there are lots of roads. Lots of people travel by car.

_____

_____

3   In Amsterdam, there isn't an underground.

_____

_____

17 me   Write sentences about you.

I want _____

_____

_____ .

I don't want _____

_____

_____ .

I want to travel by car in London. What about you?

Culture • Project

Lesson 6 Listening, Reading and Writing

18 **Listen and circle.**

Scott

1 Scott lives in:	London New York City Venice
2 Scott's favourite buildings are:	a train station a museum a swimming pool a cinema his school the shops
3 Scott goes to school by:	taxi bicycle underground

19 **Read.** **Listen and find the differences. Say stop.**

My notes:
- where I live – Bridgwater
- the buildings near where I live – shops, supermarket, cinemas, museum
- my favourite buildings – library, swimming pool
- how people travel – car, bus, bike, taxi, school bus
- how I go to school – walk

Remember!
- I go to school by { train car bus

About my town:

I live in a town called Bridgwater in the UK. It's a small town.
There are lots of shops and supermarkets. There's a cinema. There's a small museum about the history of the town.
My favourite buildings are the library and the swimming pool. I go swimming every day.
In Bridgwater, people travel by car, bus or bike. There are taxis, too. There's a school bus for children, but I walk to school.
by Caroline

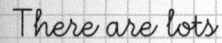 **Now write your notes and project in your notebook.**

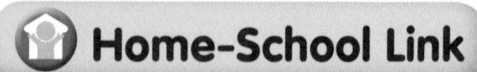 **Home-School Link**

20 **Use technology to extend your project.**

Lesson 7 Unit Review Vocabulary and Grammar

21 Look and write.

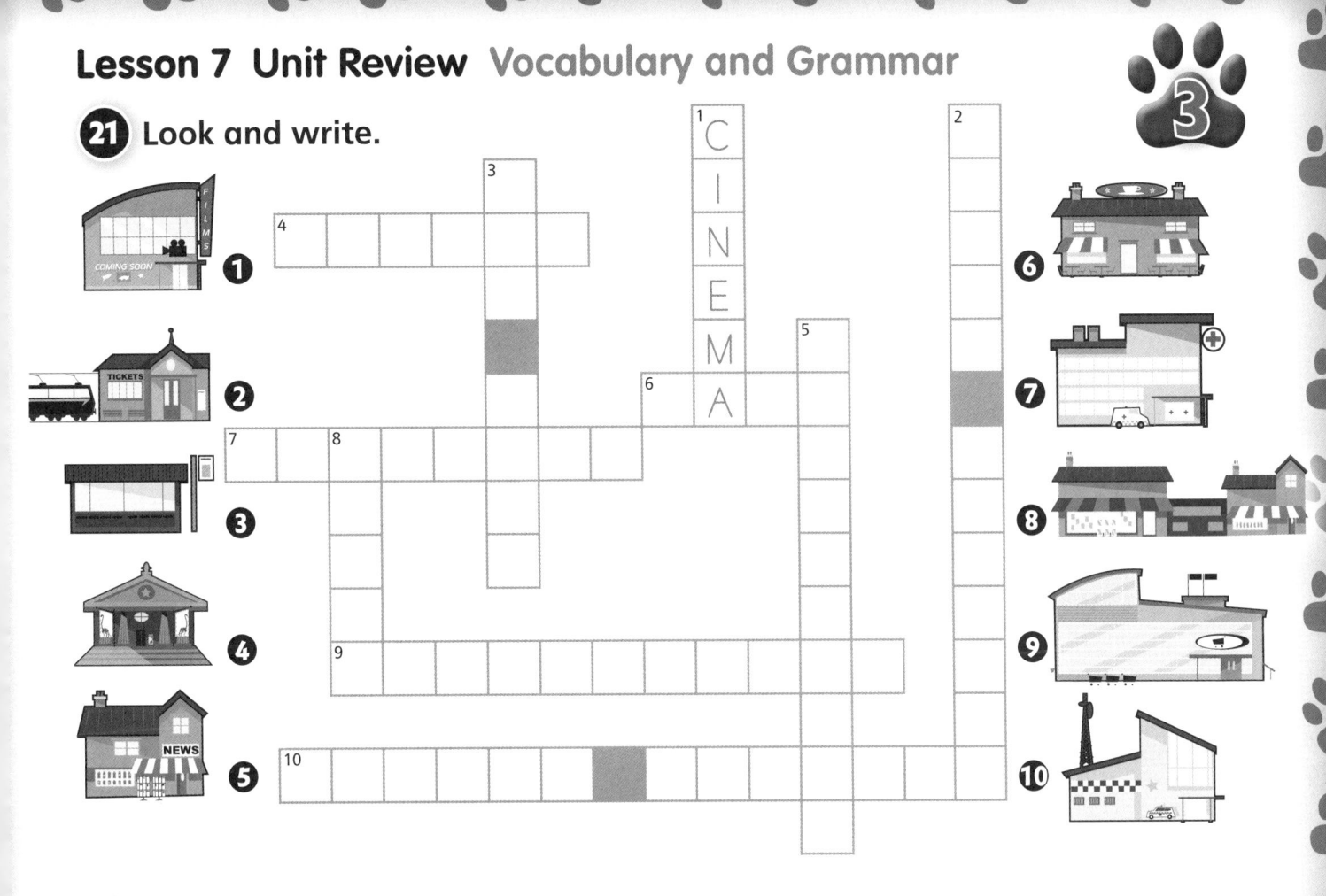

22 Read and write. CD2 21 Listen and check. Act out.

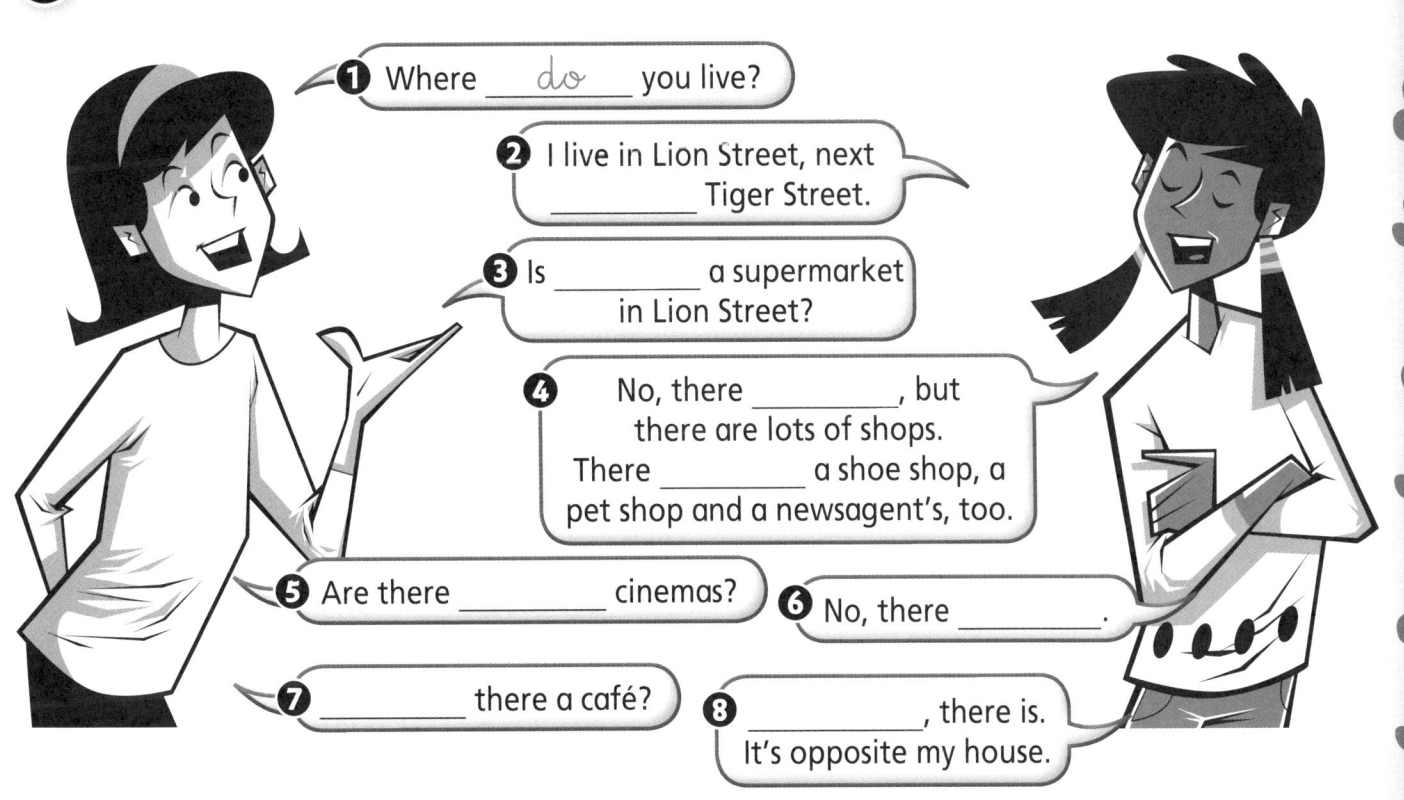

1 Where ___do___ you live?

2 I live in Lion Street, next _____ Tiger Street.

3 Is _____ a supermarket in Lion Street?

4 No, there _____, but there are lots of shops. There _____ a shoe shop, a pet shop and a newsagent's, too.

5 Are there _____ cinemas?

6 No, there _____.

7 _____ there a café?

8 _____, there is. It's opposite my house.

Lesson 8 Unit Review CLIL, Culture and Self-assessment

23 **Look and write.**

1 In London, some people travel by ____taxi____ (aitx) and the
_____ (negonudrrud).

2 In Amsterdam, some people travel by _____ (rmat), but lots of people travel
by _____ (iylbcce).

3 In Venice, some people travel by _____ (odlgnoa), but lots of people travel
by _____ _____ (aewtr usb).

24 **Read and write.** 🎵 CD2 22 **Listen and check.**

> place   ~~My~~   in   are   a   by   of

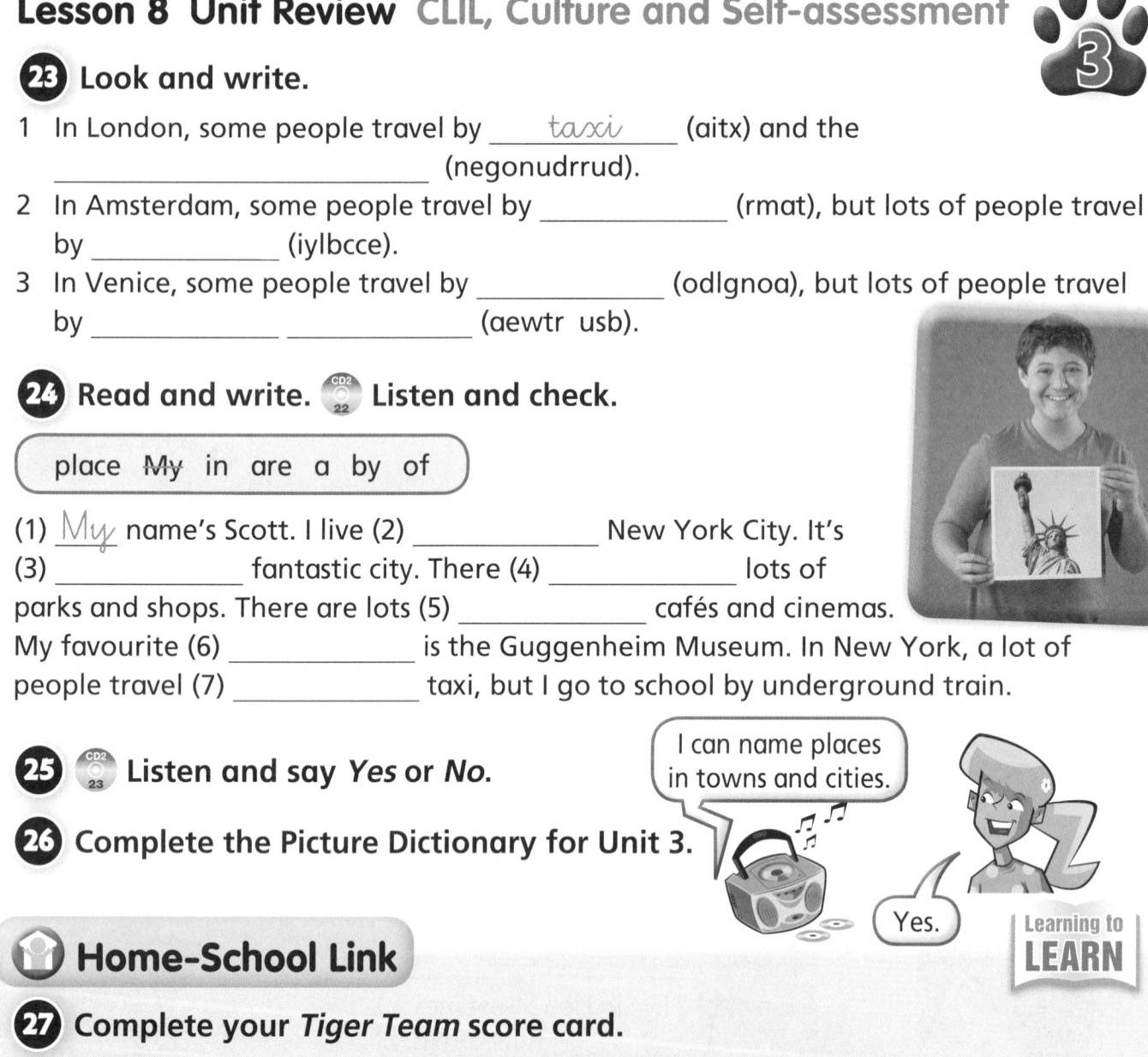

(1) _My_ name's Scott. I live (2) _____ New York City. It's
(3) _____ fantastic city. There (4) _____ lots of
parks and shops. There are lots (5) _____ cafés and cinemas.
My favourite (6) _____ is the Guggenheim Museum. In New York, a lot of
people travel (7) _____ taxi, but I go to school by underground train.

25 🎵 CD2 23 **Listen and say *Yes* or *No*.**

> I can name places
> in towns and cities.

26 **Complete the Picture Dictionary for Unit 3.**

> Yes.

Learning to
LEARN

🏠 **Home-School Link**

27 **Complete your *Tiger Team* score card.**

My Tiger Team score card

My work in Unit 3 is:	My Learning Plan
OK ⭐	I plan to:
Good ⭐⭐	☐ read Unit 3 again
Very good ⭐⭐⭐	☐ write a list of words to remember
Excellent ⭐⭐⭐⭐	☐ learn the grammar table
	☐ do the online activities

28 **Do an activity from your Learning Plan and complete your *Progress Journal* for Unit 3.**

4 Jobs and Routines

Lesson 1 Vocabulary

1 Find, circle and write.

1 _farmer_

2 _____

3 _____

4 _____

5 _____

6 _____

i	o	s	h	o	p	a	s	s	i	s	t	a	n	t
g	c	n	x	g	o	p	h	p	u	m	i	u	l	p
f	v	l	t	w	l	v	o	w	f	o	n	h	d	j
i	n	p	b	t	i	z	a	e	h	a	j	u	w	g
r	e	o	f	a	c	q	d	b	m	b	r	f	g	j
e	b	p	d	x	e	a	c	d	z	i	t	m	o	k
f	a	s	h	i	o	n	d	e	s	i	g	n	e	r
i	v	t	b	d	f	y	e	s	h	e	k	r	m	r
g	w	a	m	r	f	d	b	i	t	d	t	y	j	s
h	q	r	o	i	i	s	n	g	s	l	f	i	l	h
t	y	n	s	v	c	t	v	n	u	r	s	e	w	p
e	x	z	q	e	e	a	x	e	l	f	g	r	j	k
r	c	e	a	r	r	s	p	r	u	q	k	v	e	t

7 _____

8 _____

9 _____

10 _____

2 Look. Write the first letter and find the sentence.

M y _____ .

3 Look and write.

1 He works in a museum.

2 _____

3 She _____

4 _____

4 Lesson 2 An animal story

A Visitor at School

4 Write and match.

1 What does Lulu do? Can you ____ *guess* ____?

2 Put the _____ away, Donna.

3 Let's go into the _____ and find out.

4 I think this is very _____. I love dogs.

a

b

c

d

5 Order and write. CD2 28 Listen and check.

1 Lulu / design / doesn't / clothes
   Lulu doesn't design clothes.

2 a / designer / isn't / She / fashion
   _____

3 doctor / She / a / isn't / or / nurse / a
   _____

4 doesn't / hospital / She / in / a / work
   _____

5 doesn't / a / wear / She / uniform
   _____

6 a / officer / police / isn't / She
   _____

7 is / guide / Lulu / a / dog
   _____

8 Julie / She / helps / in / different / many / ways
   _____

🏠 Home-School Link

6 🙂 Read and reflect. Write. 💻 online materials

1 I think it _____ (is / isn't) very important to find out about different jobs.

2 I think the story is _____ (sweet / interesting / funny / …).

3 My favourite moment in the story is _____.

4 I think guide dogs are _____.

7 Write six words from the story. Tell your family what they mean.

1 _____   2 _____   3 _____

4 _____   5 _____   6 _____

Lesson 3 Grammar and Writing

Grrr... is for Grammar! 4

8 **Read and write. Learn.**

He (1) _works_ on a farm.

He (2) _____ work in a hospital.

(3) _____ he work with animals?

Yes, he (4) _____.   (5) _____, he doesn't.

Tiger Tips
Remember!
• He / She works ...
• He / She doesn't work ...

9 **Look and write.** CD2 30 **Listen and check.**

1 _Does_ he work on a farm?   _Yes, he does._

2 _____ he wear a uniform?   _____

3 _____ he work with animals?   _____

4 _____ he a farmer?   _____

5 _____ she work in a school?   _____

6 _____ she wear special clothes?   _____

7 _____ she work with computers?   _____

8 _____ she a firefighter?   _____

10 **Circle the different job. Write.**

astronaut firefighter (taxi driver)	1 I think _____ 'taxi driver' _____ is different. _A taxi driver doesn't wear special clothes._
vet police officer farmer	2 I think _____ is different. A _____.
police officer teacher taxi driver	3 I think _____ is different. A _____.
nurse web designer fashion designer	4 I think _____ is different. A _____.

31

11 Remember, write and say.

Fantastic Phonics

VICTOR THE VET

Frank the _____

Victor the _____

12 Read and match. 🔊 CD2 34 Listen and check.

1 He wears …   got a dog.
2 He drives …   a police station.
3 He works …   police officer.
4 He doesn't work …   a police car.
5 He works in …   in a shop.
6 He has …   a uniform.
7 He's a …   with people.

🏠 **Home-School Link**

13 Look, read and write.

Does she work inside?
What's her job?
~~Does she work with animals?~~
Does she wear a uniform?

1 *Does she work with animals?*   No, she doesn't.
2 _____   No, she doesn't. But she wears special clothes.
3 _____   Yes, she does. But she works outside, too.
4 _____   She's a pop star.

14 Practise the dialogue at home with your family.

Lesson 5 Reading, Writing and Grammar

15 Look and write.

1 This is Rex. He's a
_____*guide dog*_____.

2 This is Sandy. She's a
_____.

3 This is Todd. He's a
_____.

16 Read and write.

> farmer   harness   pavements   ~~nose~~   team   whistles

1 A mountain rescue dog uses its _____*nose*_____ to find people in the mountains.

2 A mountain rescue dog works with a _____ of rescue workers.

3 A guide dog guides its owner along the _____ and stops at roads.

4 A guide dog wears a _____.

5 A sheepdog works with a sheep _____.

6 A sheepdog understands the farmer when he _____.

17 Read and circle.

Max is a hearing dog. His owner, Sylvia, is deaf. She cannot hear. Max tells Sylvia when a telephone or an alarm clock rings. Max tells her when someone says her name. In the street, Max tells Sylvia when he hears a siren. Max puts his paw on his owner's leg to communicate.

1 Max is a guide dog.   True   (False)
2 Sylvia cannot hear.   True   False
3 Max works with his ears.   True   False
4 Max guides Sylvia along the pavement.   True   False
5 Max makes a noise to communicate with Sylvia.   True   False
6 Max puts his paw on Sylvia's leg to communicate.   True   False

18 Write sentences about working dogs.

_____

_____

_____

Culture • Project

Lesson 6 Listening, Reading and Writing

19 Read. 🔵 CD2 38 **Listen and tick (✓).**

Ben

Ben's aunt

1 Ben's aunt works in a shop. ☐

2 She wears a uniform. ☐

3 She doesn't wear a uniform. ☐

4 She works in a hospital. ☐

5 She drives a bus. ☐

6 She works with animals. ☐

7 She works in a zoo. ☐

8 She works on a farm. ☐

20 Read. 🔵 CD2 39 **Listen and find the differences. Say stop.**

 My sister

 Mr Thomas

My notes:

- the person's name — my sister, Mr Thomas
- what his / her job is — bus driver (sister), shop assistant (Mr T.)
- where he / she works — bus station (sister), sweet shop (Mr T.)
- what he / she wears — uniform (sister), no uniform (Mr T.)
- what he / she does — drives a bus (sister), helps people in the shop (Mr T.)

Remember!

- My brother is **a** policeman. ✓
- My brother is policeman. ✗

People who work in my town:

My sister is a bus driver. She works at the bus station in the town centre. She wears a uniform. She drives a big blue bus. She works from nine to five, from Monday to Friday. She doesn't work at the weekend. She's very good at her job. Mr Thomas is a shop assistant. He works in a sweet shop in my street. He doesn't wear a uniform. He helps people in the shop. He works from Monday to Saturday. He's a nice man and he's very good at his job.
by Emma

✏️ **Now write your notes and project in your notebook.**

🏠 **Home-School Link**

21 🖱️ **Use technology to extend your project.**

Lesson 7 Unit Review Vocabulary and Grammar

22 Look and write the letters. Match.

1	2	3	4	5	6	7	8	9	10	11	12	13	14	15	16	17	18	19	20	21	22	23	24	25	26
a	b	c	d	e	f	g	h	i	j	k	l	m	n	o	p	q	r	s	t	u	v	w	x	y	z

1 14 - 21 - 18 - 19 - 5

   n u r s e _____   *i*

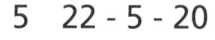

2 16 - 15 - 12 - 9 - 3 - 5   15 - 6 - 6 - 9 - 3 - 5 - 18

_____

3 16 - 15 - 16   19 - 20 - 1 - 18

_____

4 6 - 1 - 19 - 8 - 9 - 15 - 14   4 - 5 - 19 - 9 - 7 - 14 - 5 - 18

_____

5 22 - 5 - 20

_____

6 19 - 8 - 15 - 16   1 - 19 - 19 - 9 - 19 - 20 - 1 - 14 - 20

_____

7 6 - 1 - 18 - 13 - 5 - 18

_____

8 6 - 9 - 18 - 5 - 6 - 9 - 7 - 8 - 20 - 5 - 18

_____

9 20 - 1 - 24 - 9   4 - 18 - 9 - 22 - 5 - 18

_____

10 23 - 5 - 2   4 - 5 - 19 - 9 - 7 - 14 - 5 - 18

_____

23 Read and circle. 🔊 CD2 43 Listen and check. Act out.

1 Does your uncle (work) / works in a shop?

2 No, he doesn't. He **work** / **works** in a police station.

3 Is / **Does** he a police officer?

4 No, he **isn't** / is.

5 Does he **wear** / **wears** a uniform?

6 No, he doesn't, but he **wears** / **wear** a special hat.

7 Does **he / she** work in the canteen?

8 **Yes / No**, he does. He's a cook.

Lesson 8 Unit Review CLIL, Culture and Self-assessment

24 **Read and write.**

1 This animal helps a blind person.   *a guide dog*
2 This animal uses its nose to find people in the mountains. _____
3 This person cleans the classrooms and corridors at school. _____
4 This person prepares lunch for the pupils in a school.   _____
5 This animal helps a sheep farmer.   _____
6 This person looks after the school building.   _____

25 **Read and write.** CD2 44 **Listen and check.**

Someone who works in my town

My grandfather is (1) ____*a*____ caretaker. (2) _____ works in a school in the town centre. He doesn't (3) _____ a uniform. He looks after the school building. He repairs chairs and tables, too. He works from nine to five, from Monday to (4) _____. He (5) _____ work at the weekend. He's very good at (6) _____ job. I (7) _____ want to be a caretaker. I want to be (8) _____ teacher or a doctor.

26 CD2 45 **Listen and say *Yes* or *No*.**

I can name jobs.

27 **Complete the Picture Dictionary for Unit 4.**

Yes.

Learning to **LEARN**

🏠 Home-School Link

28 **Complete your *Tiger Team* score card.**

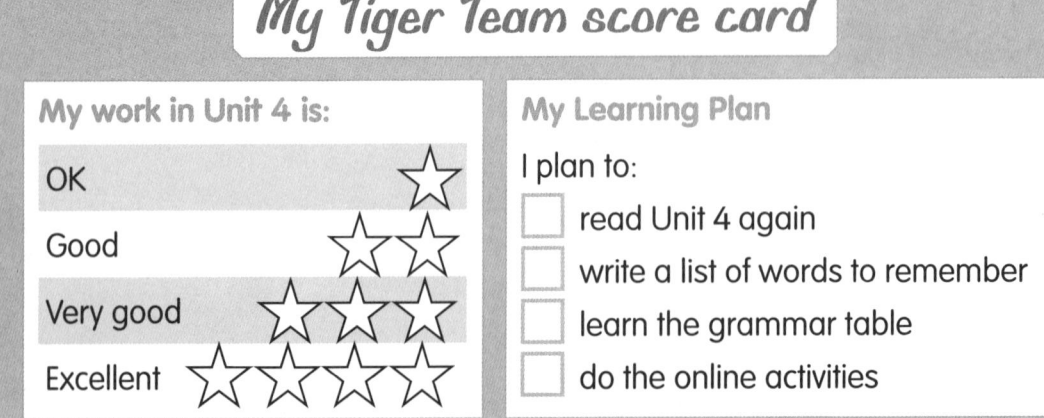

My Tiger Team score card

My work in Unit 4 is:	My Learning Plan
OK ☆	I plan to:
Good ☆☆	☐ read Unit 4 again
Very good ☆☆☆	☐ write a list of words to remember
Excellent ☆☆☆☆	☐ learn the grammar table
	☐ do the online activities

29 **Do an activity from your Learning Plan and complete your *Progress Journal* for Unit 4.**

5 Things We Like Doing

Lesson 1 Vocabulary

1 Look and write.

1 *reading comics*   2 _____   3 _____   4 _____   5 _____

6 _____   7 _____   8 _____   9 _____   10 _____

2 ♻ Look. Write the first letter and find the sentence.

 8

M y

 3 __ __ 90

_____ .

3 Look and write.

1 *His favourite activity is reading comics.*

2 *Her favourite activity is* _____

3 _____

4 _____

Lesson 2 A true story

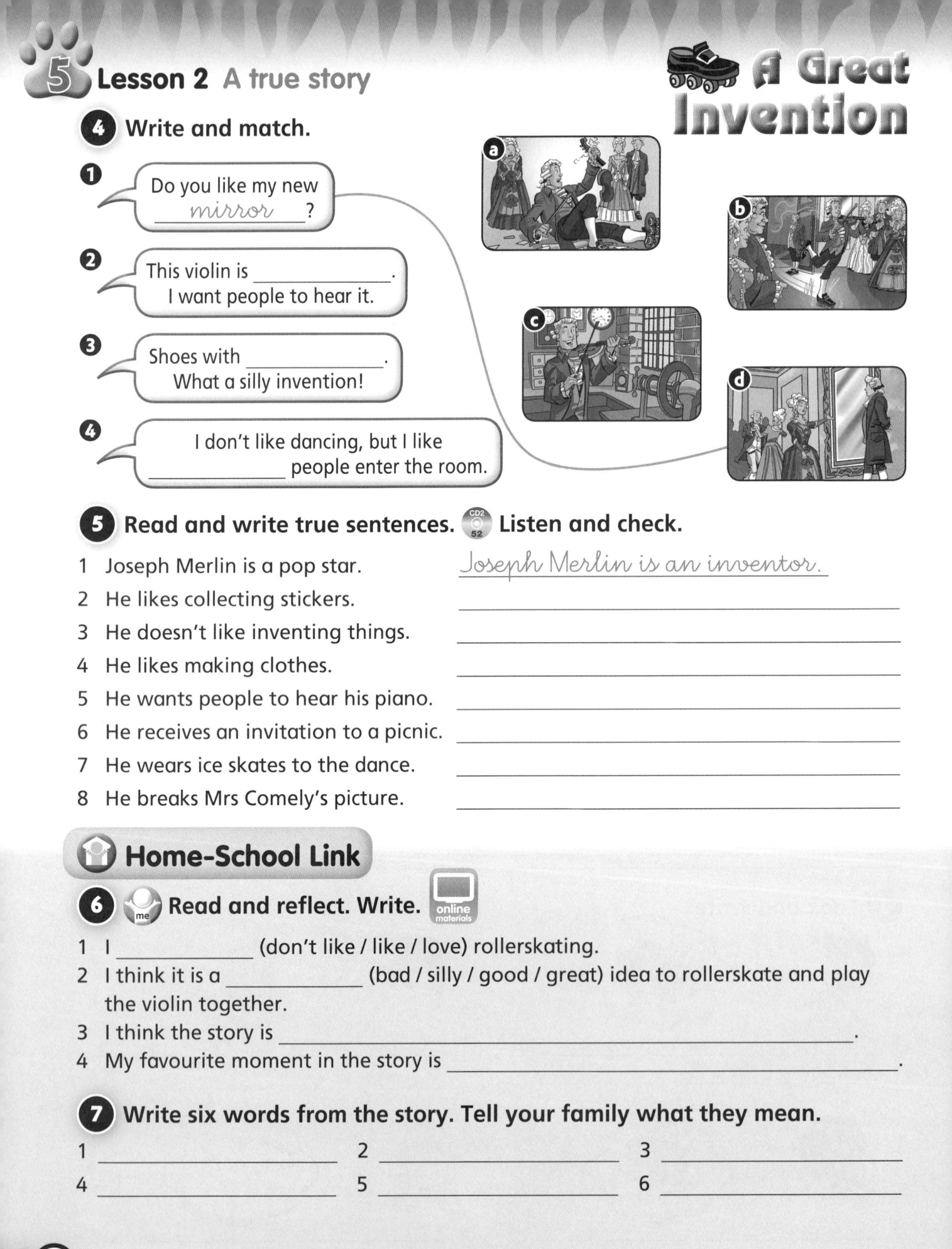

A Great Invention

4 Write and match.

1
Do you like my new ___*mirror*___ ?

2
This violin is _____.
I want people to hear it.

3
Shoes with _____.
What a silly invention!

4
I don't like dancing, but I like _____ people enter the room.

5 Read and write true sentences. CD2 52 Listen and check.

1 Joseph Merlin is a pop star. ___*Joseph Merlin is an inventor.*___

2 He likes collecting stickers. _____

3 He doesn't like inventing things. _____

4 He likes making clothes. _____

5 He wants people to hear his piano. _____

6 He receives an invitation to a picnic. _____

7 He wears ice skates to the dance. _____

8 He breaks Mrs Comely's picture. _____

🏠 Home-School Link

6 Read and reflect. Write. online materials

1 I _____ (don't like / like / love) rollerskating.
2 I think it is a _____ (bad / silly / good / great) idea to rollerskate and play the violin together.
3 I think the story is _____.
4 My favourite moment in the story is _____.

7 Write six words from the story. Tell your family what they mean.

1 _____   2 _____   3 _____
4 _____   5 _____   6 _____

Lesson 3 Grammar and Writing

Grrr... is for Grammar! 5

8 Read and write. Learn.

I (1) ___like___ rollerskating.

I (2) _____ like painting pictures.

(3) _____ you like reading comics? Yes, I do. No, I (4) _____.

He likes dancing. He doesn't (5) _____ shopping.

She (6) _____ shopping. She (7) _____ like dancing.

Tiger Tips

Remember!

- *I like ...*
  He / She likes ...
- *I don't like ...*
  He / She doesn't like ...

9 Look, read and write. CD2 54 Listen and check.

1 Do you like reading comics, Oliver?
___Yes, I do.___

2 Do you like dancing? _____

3 Do you like taking photos?
_____ I love taking photos.

4 Do you like painting pictures?
_____

5 Do you like rollerskating?
_____

6 Do you like shopping? _____

10 Look and write.

1 Nasim likes taking photos.
He doesn't like dancing.
He loves collecting stickers.

2 _____
_____
_____

3 _____
_____
_____

4 _____
_____

11 Remember, write and say.

Princess Lynne _____

The king _____

12 Remember the *What do you like doing?* song. Read and write.
CD2 56 ♪ Listen and check.

What _____ *do you like doing at the* _____ weekends?
What _____ friends?
I _____ photos. | We _____ pictures.
I _____ tennis, too. | We _____ comics, too.
She _____ dancing. | They _____ computer.
He _____ shopping. | How _____ you?
How _____ you? |

🏠 Home-School Link

13 Practise the song at home with your family. online materials

14 Order and write. Look, read and circle.

CINEMA ▶

eW   kile   oging   ot
We ____ _____ __

het   nemica   yinglap
___ _____, _____

sinten   dna   lotinglrersak
_____ ___ _____

ta   het   denkwees
__ ___ _____.   True / False

Lesson 5 Reading, Writing and Grammar

15 **Read and write.**

> scientists paintings machines inventions
> sculptures artists drawings inventors

In science museums, you can find out about ...		In art galleries, you can find out about ...	
scientists			

16 **Read, write and match.**

1 This __*bicycle*__ , from 1870, is in the Science Museum in London. It hasn't got _____ or tyres.

2 This painting is in the National _____ in London. It's called _____ *in a Tropical Storm.*

3 You can play *Rock,* _____ , *scissors* with this robot in the Science _____ in London.

a. b. c. [1]

17 **Order and write.**

art · fantastic · to learn · and · science. · Museums · places · are · about

Museums _____

18 me **Read and choose. Colour.**

> I like going to art galleries.

> I like going to art galleries and science museums.

> I like going to science museums.

> I don't like going to science museums or art galleries.

Lesson 6 Listening, Reading and Writing

19 Read, think and match. Listen and check.

 Nasim

 Ellie

 Clare

 Ben

1 Nasim …   doesn't like going to museums.

2 Ellie …   likes going to science museums.

3 Clare …   likes going to art and science museums.

4 Ben …   likes going to art museums.

20 Read. Listen and find the differences. Say stop.

My notes:

- what I like doing at the weekends – football, tennis
- what I don't like doing – rollerskating
- what my favourite activity is – going to museums

Remember!

- I like swimming. I like rollerskating, too.

What I like doing at the weekends:

My name is David. At the weekends, I like playing football with my friends. I like playing tennis, too. I don't like rollerskating! My favourite activity is going to museums. There's a fantastic science museum in Valencia. There are lots of interesting things to see and it's really cool.

by David

 Now write your notes and project in your notebook.

🏠 Home-School Link

21 Use technology to extend your project.

22 Look and write.

1 *going to museums*

2 _____

3 _____

4 _____

5 _____

6 _____

7 _____

8 _____

9 _____

10 _____

23 Read and circle. 🎧 Listen and check. Act out.

1 What do you **like** / **likes** doing at the weekends?

2 I like **watching** / **watch** films with my friends.

3 **Do** / **Does** you like playing tennis or football?

4 No, I **don't** / **do**. I don't like sport.

5 What about your brother? Does **she** / **he** like sport?

6 He **loves** / **love** playing football. It's his favourite activity.

7 **Does** / **Do** he like sending text messages?

8 **No** / **Yes**, he doesn't.

Lesson 8 Unit Review CLIL, Culture and Self-assessment

24 ➡ Go to Pupil's Book page 42. Order and write.

1 ___artist___   2 s_____   3 p_____   4 d_____
(trista)   (pultscure)   (gapintin)   (warding)

5 s_____   6 i_____   7 i_____   8 r_____
(tinicests)   (tenorvin)   (ventionin)   (torbo)

25 Look, read and write. 🎵 CD3 8 Listen and check.

What I like (1) _doing_ **at the weekends**
I like rollerskating and (2) _____ tennis. I (3) _____ like
(4) _____ stickers. My favourite activity (5) _____ watching
films. I love watching films at the cinema or on DVD.
(6) _____ Ellie

26 CD3 9 Listen and say Yes or No.

27 Complete the Picture Dictionary for Unit 5.

> I can name activities I like.

> Yes.

Learning to LEARN

🎓 Home-School Link

28 Complete your *Tiger Team* score card.

My Tiger Team score card

My work in Unit 5 is:	My Learning Plan
OK ⭐	I plan to:
Good ⭐⭐	☐ read Unit 5 again
Very good ⭐⭐⭐	☐ write a list of words to remember
Excellent ⭐⭐⭐⭐	☐ learn the grammar table
	☐ do the online activities

29 Do an activity from your Learning Plan and complete your *Progress Journal* for Unit 5.

6 In the Countryside

Lesson 1 Vocabulary

1 Find, circle and write.

1 _river_

3 _____

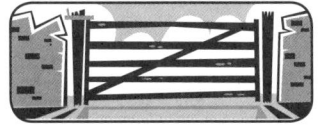

5 _____

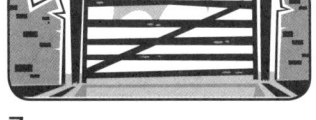

e	f	i	x	r	i	s	f	r	c	r
m	o	u	n	t	a	i	n	a	t	a
b	r	i	d	g	e	g	u	m	r	x
l	e	w	l	v	o	n	f	o	r	m
p	s	k	m	z	a	p	h	g	i	c
o	t	p	o	q	d	o	m	a	v	u
p	a	c	a	m	p	s	i	t	e	z
f	h	d	t	t	d	t	s	e	r	l
t	l	a	k	e	h	s	h	e	k	o

2 _____

4 _____

6 _____

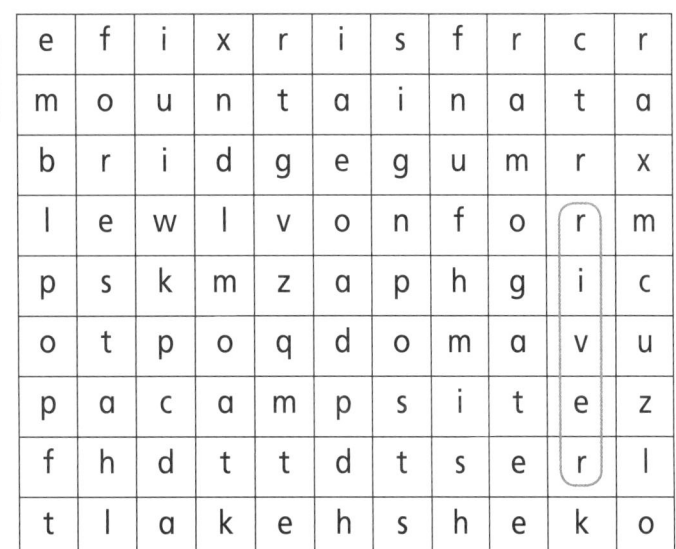

7 _____   8 _____   9 _____

10 _____

2 ♻ Look. Write the first letter and find the sentence.

🍦 🐸 🍦 👑 80 🧙 🍎 🦵 🪁 🍦 19 ▦ 🍦 99

30 🎩 🥚 🖥 🍊 ☂ 👃 🚐 🐰 🥤 66 🍦 🐕 8

_____ .

3 Read, write and match.

1 I like being in the _mountains_ (nomaintus). [c]

   a

   b

2 We love sitting next to _____ (versir). [ ]

3 I like standing on _____ (digrebs). [ ]

   c

   d

4 I like looking at the trees in the _____ (trefos). [ ]

Lesson 2 An adventure story

A **Discovery** in the Forest

4 **Read and match.** CD3 15 **Listen and check.**

1 Some children are staying ...   breaks his leg.
2 They go into the forest ...   a badger.
3 They see ...   help Mr Taylor.
4 Mr Taylor falls and ...   on a campsite.
5 The children go back ...   to a ghost orchid.
6 The rescue services ...   photo is in the newspaper.
7 Mr Taylor is lying next ...   to the campsite for help.
8 The next day, Mr Taylor's ...   with their teacher, Mr Taylor.

5 **Read, write and draw.**

1 Go to the end of this
___*path*___ (thap). Turn left.

2 Go round the _____ (kale).

3 Turn left at the
_____ (inotsgps).

4 That's the way to the
_____ (castimpe).

CAMPSITE

YOU ARE HERE

🏠 **Home-School Link**

6 👤me **Read and reflect. Write.** online materials

1 I think forests are _____ (interesting / scary) places.
2 I think it is _____ (good / bad) to pick wild flowers in the countryside.
3 My favourite moment in the story is _____.
4 I think the story is _____.

7 **Write six words from the story. Tell your family what they mean.**

1 _____   2 _____   3 _____
4 _____   5 _____   6 _____

Lesson 3 Grammar and Writing

Grrr... is for Grammar! 6

8 Read and write. Learn.

Turn left (1) __at__ the bridge.

(2) _____ turn right.

Go to the (3) _____ of the path.

Do I go straight (4) _____?

(5) _____ we go over the bridge?

Tiger Tips
Remember!
- Turn left.
- Don't turn right.

9 Order and write. CD3 18 Listen and check.

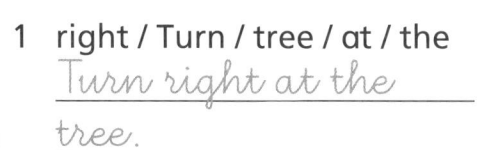

1 right / Turn / tree / at / the
Turn right at the
tree.

2 to / the / go / end / of /
path / the / ? / I / Do
_____
_____

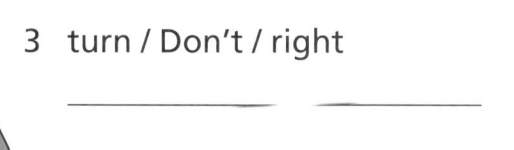

3 turn / Don't / right
_____
_____

4 go / on / straight / we /
Do / ?
_____
_____

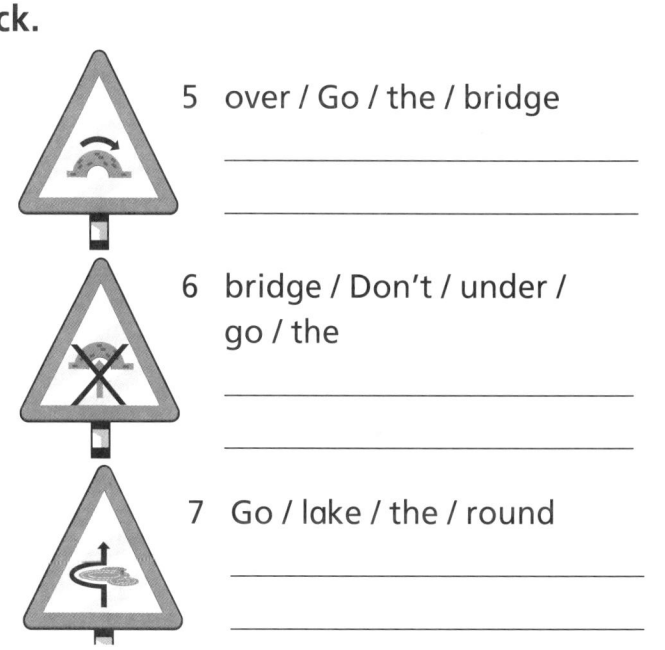

5 over / Go / the / bridge
_____
_____

6 bridge / Don't / under /
go / the
_____
_____

7 Go / lake / the / round
_____
_____

10 Look and write.

1 _Turn left at the river._

2 _____

3 _____

4 _____

❶ ❷

❸ ❹

11 Remember, write and say.

Fantastic Phonics

RIVER

Don't ...

Do not ...

A ghost _____

A dog _____

12 Remember *The way to the campsite* song. Read and write.
CD3 20 🎵 Listen and check.

Excuse me. We're _____
And it's a very dark _____.
Do you _____ the way to the campsite?
Go _____ on.
Go to the _____ of the path.
Don't go over the _____.
Go _____ the farm.
Turn left _____ the river.
And then turn _____.
That's the _____ to the campsite.
Yes, that's the way to the _____.

Pop Spot

Home-School Link

13 Practise the song at home with your family. online materials

14 Look, read and write. CD3 22 Listen and check. Order.

a That's the way to the ___farm___. ☐

b Go round the _____. ☐

c Go straight on and turn right at the _____. ☐

d Yes, I can. Go to the end of this _____ and turn right. ☐

e Excuse me, can you tell me the way to the _____? ☐ 1

f Go over the _____ and then turn left. Don't turn right. ☐

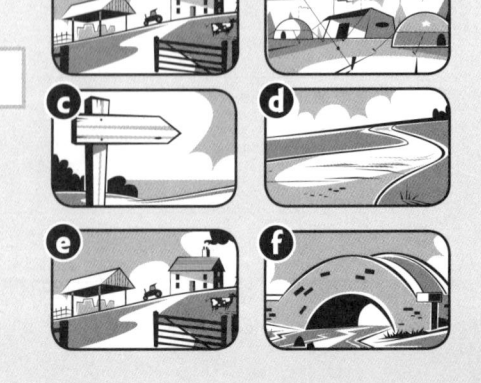

Lesson 5 Reading, Writing and Grammar

CLIL
Natural Science

15 Read and write.

| A squirrel A mushroom Mistletoe A woodpecker A beetle | insect plant mammal bird fungus |

1 *A squirrel is a mammal.*
2 _____
3 _____
4 _____
5 _____

16 Read and write true sentences.

1 Mistletoe grows on tree leaves.
 Mistletoe grows on tree branches.

2 Beetles lay their eggs in tall trees.
 _____

3 All mushrooms grow on tree trunks.
 _____

4 Squirrels live in houses in trees.
 _____

5 Woodpeckers eat mushrooms.
 _____

17 Order and write.

S E E T R C P   N D A   R P E O T T C   S S O E T R F
R e s p e c t ___ _____ _____

O T N ' D   U C T   W D N O   E E T S R
____ ' ___ ____ _____

18  Write sentences about what you prefer.

I like walking in the forest, but I prefer walking in the mountains.

_____
_____
_____

Lesson 6 Listening, Reading and Writing

19 **Listen and match.**

1
Billy

2
Tessa

3
Kate

4
Dan

a
Come to the beach this summer. Don't forget your sun cream.

b
Come to the campsite this summer. There's lots of wildlife to see.

c
Come to London by bus this summer. Remember to bring your camera.

d
Relax on one of England's canals.

20 **Read.** CD3 27 **Listen and find the differences. Say stop.**

My notes:
- where I want to go – Brighton, UK
- what's there and what I like doing there – the beach, shops, cafés, friends, campsite; swimming

Remember!
- There's a café. = There is a café.

My ideal holiday destination:

I want to go to Brighton for the summer holiday.
Brighton is a city by the sea. It's 45 minutes from London by train. There are lots of shops and cafés in Brighton. There's a beach. We like swimming in the sea. The water is cold, but it's a lot of fun. We stay in a tent at a campsite. I've got friends there.
by Annabel

 Now write your notes and project in your notebook.

🏠 **Home-School Link**

21 **Use technology to extend your project.**

Lesson 7 Unit Review Vocabulary and Grammar

22 Look and write.

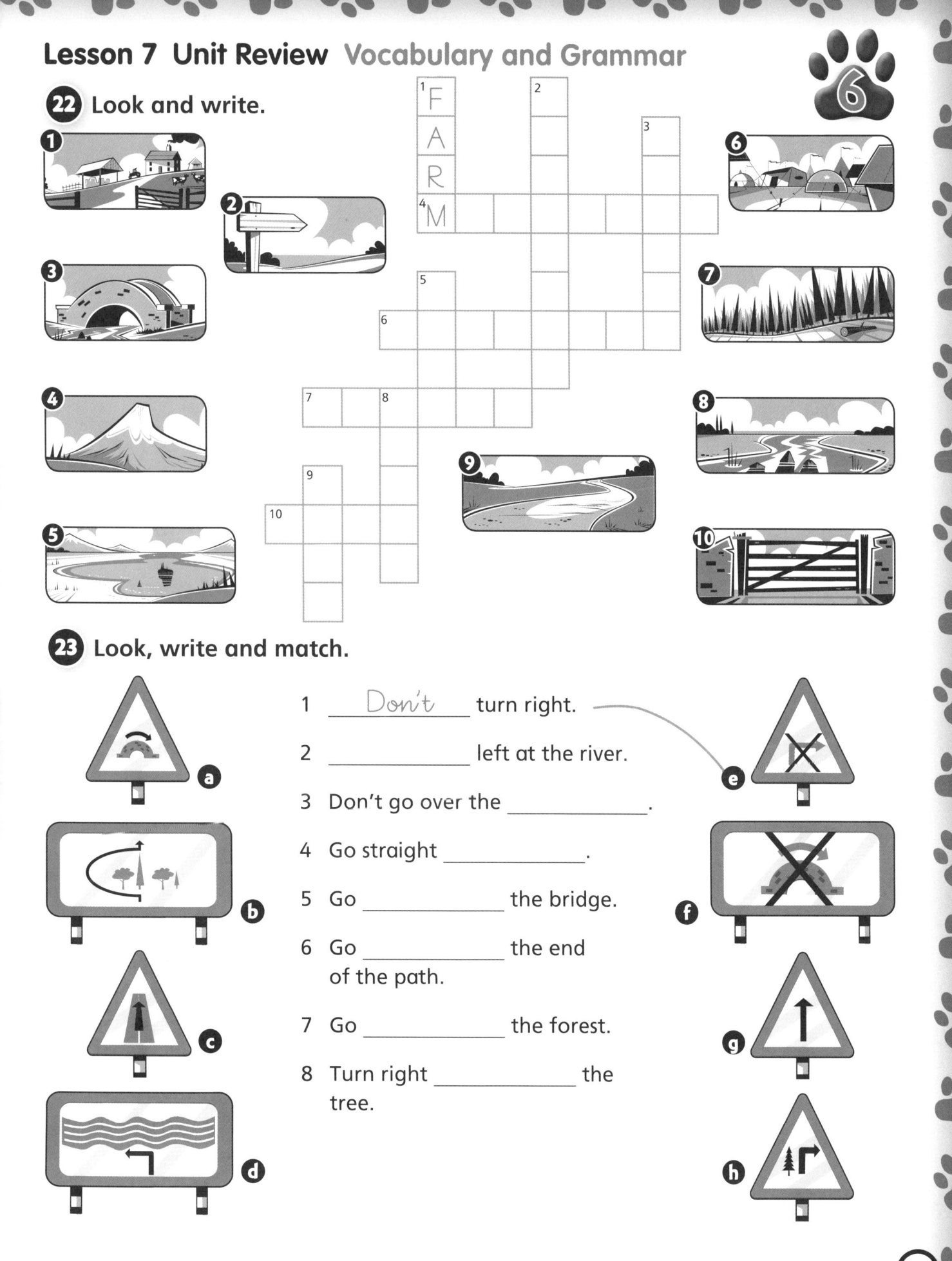

23 Look, write and match.

1 _____Don't_____ turn right.

2 _____ left at the river.

3 Don't go over the _____.

4 Go straight _____.

5 Go _____ the bridge.

6 Go _____ the end of the path.

7 Go _____ the forest.

8 Turn right _____ the tree.

Lesson 8 Unit Review CLIL, Culture and Self-assessment

24 **Look and write.**

¹B	E	E	T	L	E
			R		
			E		
			E		
			S		

25 **Read and write.** (CD3 31) **Listen and check.**

In the UK …

School finishes at the beginning of (1) _____July_____ (luJy).
The summer holiday is (2) _____ (xis)
weeks long. Many children go to the (3) _____
(cheab) or to a (4) _____ (pitescam). Some children stay with their
(5) _____ (parentsdrang). Some children go to other (6) _____
(ountcries) with their family. Everyone's holiday is (7) _____ (ferifdent).

26 (CD3 32) **Listen and say *Yes* or *No*.**

27 **Complete the Picture Dictionary for Unit 6.**

> I can name things you see in the countryside.

> Yes.

Learning to **LEARN**

🏠 **Home-School Link**

28 **Complete your *Tiger Team* score card.**

My Tiger Team score card

My work in Unit 6 is:	My Learning Plan
OK ⭐	I plan to:
Good ⭐⭐	☐ read Unit 6 again
Very good ⭐⭐⭐	☐ write a list of words to remember
Excellent ⭐⭐⭐⭐	☐ learn the grammar table
	☐ do the online activities

29 **Do an activity from your Learning Plan and complete your *Progress Journal* for Unit 6.**

7 Tiger Street Club Review

Lesson 1 Vocabulary

1 Find, circle and write.

WIGSDIRECTORMAKE-UPARTISTCAMERAMANSCREENPLAY

ACTRESSCLAPPERBOARDCAMERAWRITERSPECIALEFFECTS

1 _____ 2 _____ 3 _____ 4 _____ 5 _____

6 _____ 7 _____ 8 _wigs_ 9 _____ 10 _____

2 Look. Write the first letter and find the sentence.

3  Read and write answers for you. Ask a friend.

1 Do you like watching films?

_____

2 Can you spell _____ ?

_____

3 Have you got a camera?

_____

4 Do you want to be an actor?

_____

7 Lesson 2 A screenplay

4 **Read and number in order.** CD3 36 **Listen and check.**

The children look at photos of cities around the world. ☐

Sara calls the fire brigade. ☐

The next day, Phileas and his flying machine are famous. ☐

Sara flies around the world with Phileas. ☐

The fire brigade rescue Mr Jones, the caretaker, and they put out the fire. ☐

They see a photo of a fire at their school. ☐

The other children laugh at him. ☐

Phileas is making a flying machine. ☐ 1

5 ➜ **Go to Pupil's Book page 54. Read and write.**

1 _Has_ Phileas got blue hair?
   No, he hasn't. He's got red hair.

2 _____ Sara hate flying?
   _____

3 _____ there twenty seats in the flying machine?
   _____

4 _____ the flying machine fly around the world in seventy seconds?
   _____

5 _____ Mr Jones a teacher?
   _____

🏠 Home-School Link

6 me **Read and reflect. Write.** online materials

1 I _____ (want / don't want) to travel around the world.
2 I think it _____ (is / isn't) nice to laugh at people.
3 I think the screenplay is _____.
4 I think Phileas is _____.

7 **Write six words from the story. Tell your family what they mean.**

1 _____   2 _____   3 _____
4 _____   5 _____   6 _____

8 Make your own *Tiger Street Club* 'can do' board game. Write questions. Play with a friend.

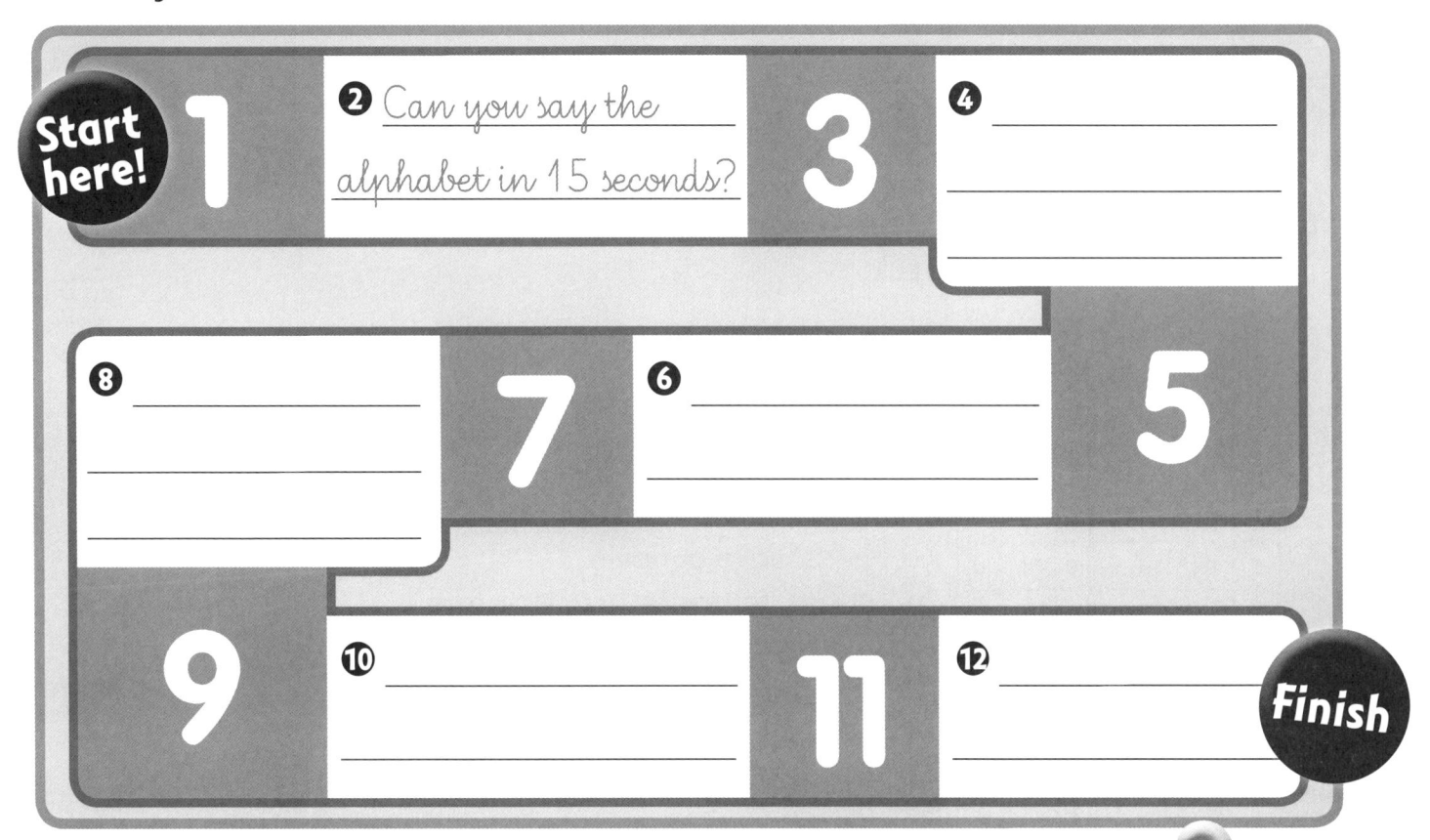

Start here!

1

2 Can you say the alphabet in 15 seconds?

3

4 _____

8 _____

7

6 _____

5

9

10 _____

11

12 _____

Finish

9 Read and write the answers to the *Tiger Street Club quiz*.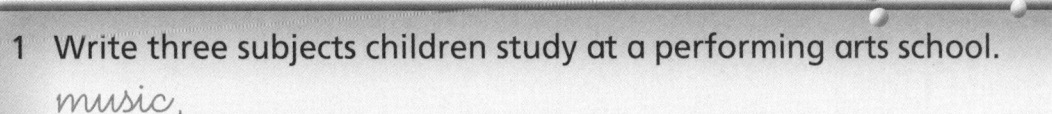

1 Write three subjects children study at a performing arts school.

music, _____

2 Write three things you can borrow from a library in the UK.

_____

3 Write a common type of transport in Venice.

_____

4 Write four jobs that people do in your school.

_____

5 Write three things you can see in an art gallery.

_____

6 Write three animals that live in trees. Write two things that grow on trees.

_____

Lesson 4 Grammar, Listening and Writing

10 **Remember, match and say. Colour.**

Fantastic Phonics

A E I O U

yellow ☐ blue ☐ white ☐ grey Ⓐ green ☐

11 **Remember the *Let's make a movie* song. Find, circle and write.**
CD3 39 🎵 **Listen and check.**

b	c	d	u	s	e	m	y
a	l	z	p	c	h	a	f
c	a	m	e	r	a	k	r
t	p	o	t	e	x	e	b
r	p	k	j	e	l	u	o
e	e	z	q	n	m	p	g
s	r	s	u	p	e	a	c
s	b	k	a	l	m	r	x
x	o	r	c	a	w	t	n
q	a	f	t	y	i	i	p
g	r	m	o	p	g	s	w
v	d	f	r	a	s	t	i
d	i	r	e	c	t	o	r

I've got a ___screenplay___.
You've got a _____.
I know an _____.
You know an _____.
Let's make a movie.
A fun, fantastic, groovy movie
With lots of special effects!
I've got a _____.
You've got _____.
We know a _____.
And a _____.
Let's make a movie.
A fun, fantastic, groovy movie
With lots of special effects!

Pop Spot

🏠 Home-School Link

12 **Practise the song at home with your family.** online materials

13 **Order and write.**

Greg
we've got =
we have got

1 playground / We've / with / got / grammar / Greg / in / the
___We've___
_____

2 pool / The / likes / in / his / singing / pink / swimming / king
_____
_____

Lesson 5 Reading, Writing and Grammar

CLIL

ICT

14 ➡ **Go to Pupil's Book page 58. Look, read and write.**

1 What's his job?

He's a director.

He directs the actors and the _____ .

2 What's his job?

He's _____

He writes the _____ .

3 What's her job?

_____

She helps the actors with their _____ and make-up.

4 What's his job?

_____

He _____ the film.

5 What's her job?

_____

She _____ in the film.

15 **Look and write.**

download digital camera computer

1 _____

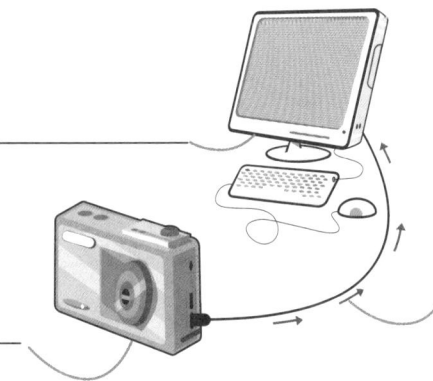

3 _____

2 _____

16 **Read and write answers for you. Ask a friend.**

Have you got an idea for a simple screenplay?

Yes, I have.

1 Do you like films? _____

2 Have you got an idea for a simple screenplay? _____

3 Can you use a digital camera and a computer? _____

Culture • Project

Lesson 6 Listening, Reading and Writing

17 CD3 44 **Listen and circle.**

Tell me about *Tiger Team 4*.

1	grammar activities:	good	(very good)	great
2	stories:	great	enjoyable	nice
3	songs:	cool	excellent	fantastic
4	DVD:	good	interesting	brilliant
5	Fantastic Phonics:	funny	amazing	memorable

18 **Read.** CD3 45 **Listen and find the differences. Say stop.**

My notes:
- Am I happy with my progress in English? – yes, very happy
- What is my favourite Tiger Team 4 story / song? – Unit 6 song, Unit 3 story
- What do I find difficult / easy in English? – difficult: speaking activities, easy: listening activities, reading activities, writing activities

Remember!
- Use capital letters in story titles.
The Piper of Hamlin

My English report:

I'm very happy with my progress in English. I like Tiger Team 4. It's enjoyable and interesting. My favourite story is The Piper of Hamlin in Unit 3 and my favourite song is The way to the campsite in Unit 6. The things I find difficult are the speaking activities. The things I find easy are the listening, reading and writing activities.
I like learning English. It's my favourite subject.
by Scott

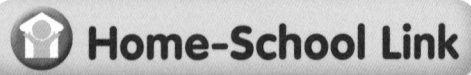 **Now write your notes and project in your notebook.**

🏠 Home-School Link

19 🖱 **Use technology to extend your project.**

20 Look and write.

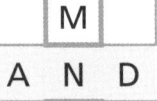  

Crossword:

1. S P E C I A L E F F E C T S
   Down: F I L M A N D C I N E M A

21 Read and write.

Around the World in Eighty Minutes

A boy called Phileas likes inventing things. The other children think Phileas is _strange_. They laugh at him. One day, Phileas invents a flying _____. It can fly around the world in eighty _____. Sara flies with Phileas.

The other children look at photos from the digital _____. They see photos of London, Venice and many other cities, _____ and villages around the _____.

The children see a photo of their school. It's on _____. Mr Jones, the _____, is painting the corridors. Sara calls the fire _____. They rescue Mr Jones and put out the fire.

The next day, Phileas and his flying machine are on the cover of every _____. And now, the other children think Phileas is _____.

22 → Go to Pupil's Book page 58. Order, write and match.

1 The / the / writer / screenplay / writes
The writer writes the screenplay.

2 actors / director / The / directs the / and / the / cameraman
_____
_____

3 actors / act / The / in / film / the
_____

4 film / The / shoots / cameraman / the
_____

23 Look, read and write.

You can shoot a home movie with a digital (1) _____ (aeacmr).
You can (2) _____ (oonddalw) your movie onto your
(3) _____ (optrcmue).

24 Complete the Picture Dictionary for Unit 7.

25 CD3 49 Listen and say *Yes* or *No*.

I can name things related to making movies.

Yes.

Learning to **LEARN**

Home-School Link

26 Complete your *Tiger Team* score card.

My Tiger Team score card

My work in Unit 7 is:	My Learning Plan
OK ☆	I plan to:
Good ☆☆	☐ read Unit 7 again
Very good ☆☆☆	☐ write a list of words to remember
Excellent ☆☆☆☆☆	☐ look at all my work in *Tiger Team 4*
	☐ practise English in the holidays

27 Do an activity from your Learning Plan and complete your *Progress Journal* for Unit 7.

REFERENCE AND EXTENSION MATERIAL WITH EXAM PRACTICE

Verb List

Translate these verbs into your language.

to borrow	_____	to prefer	_____
to break	_____	to prepare	_____
to clean	_____	to promise	_____
to collect stickers	_____	to put	_____
to dance	_____	to read comics	_____
to describe	_____	to remember	_____
to design	_____	to repair	_____
to download	_____	to rescue	_____
to drive	_____	to return	_____
to fall	_____	to rollerskate	_____
to find	_____	to say	_____
to find out	_____	to shop	_____
to finish	_____	to sit	_____
to fly	_____	to stand	_____
to forget	_____	to stay	_____
to give	_____	to study	_____
to go back	_____	to take	_____
to go to museums	_____	to take photos	_____
to guide	_____	to talk about	_____
to hear	_____	to talk to friends	_____
to help	_____	to teach	_____
to imagine	_____	to tell	_____
to invent	_____	to touch	_____
to keep a promise	_____	to travel	_____
to laugh at	_____	to turn left / right	_____
to learn	_____	to understand	_____
to like	_____	to use the computer	_____
to listen	_____	to visit	_____
to live	_____	to walk	_____
to look after	_____	to want	_____
to look at	_____	to watch films	_____
to make a movie	_____	to wear	_____
to paint pictures	_____	to work	_____
to play the recorder	_____	to write stories	_____

Picture Dictionary

Starter Unit

	twenty		forty	

sixty		eighty		a hundred

Unit 1

	science		art and design	

ICT		history		drama

Unit 2

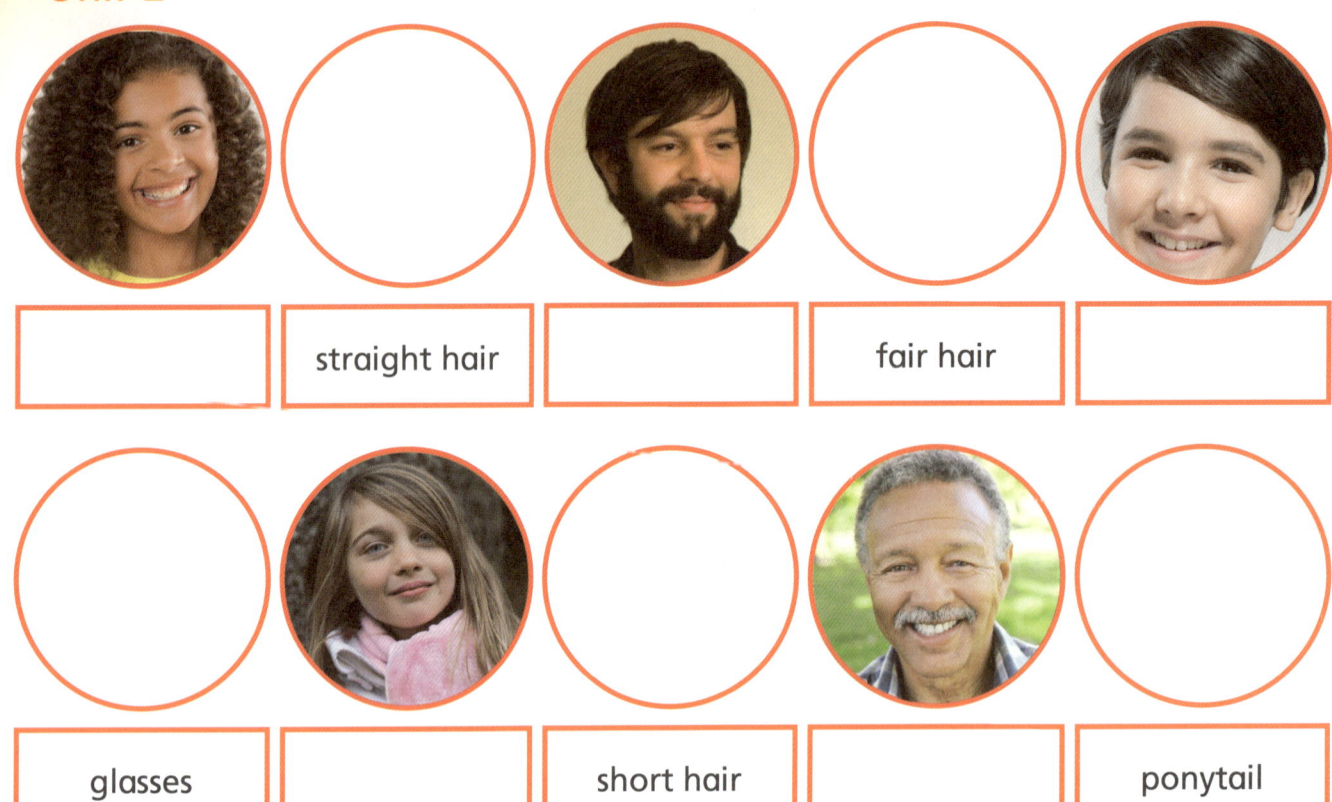

	straight hair		fair hair	

glasses		short hair		ponytail

Unit 3

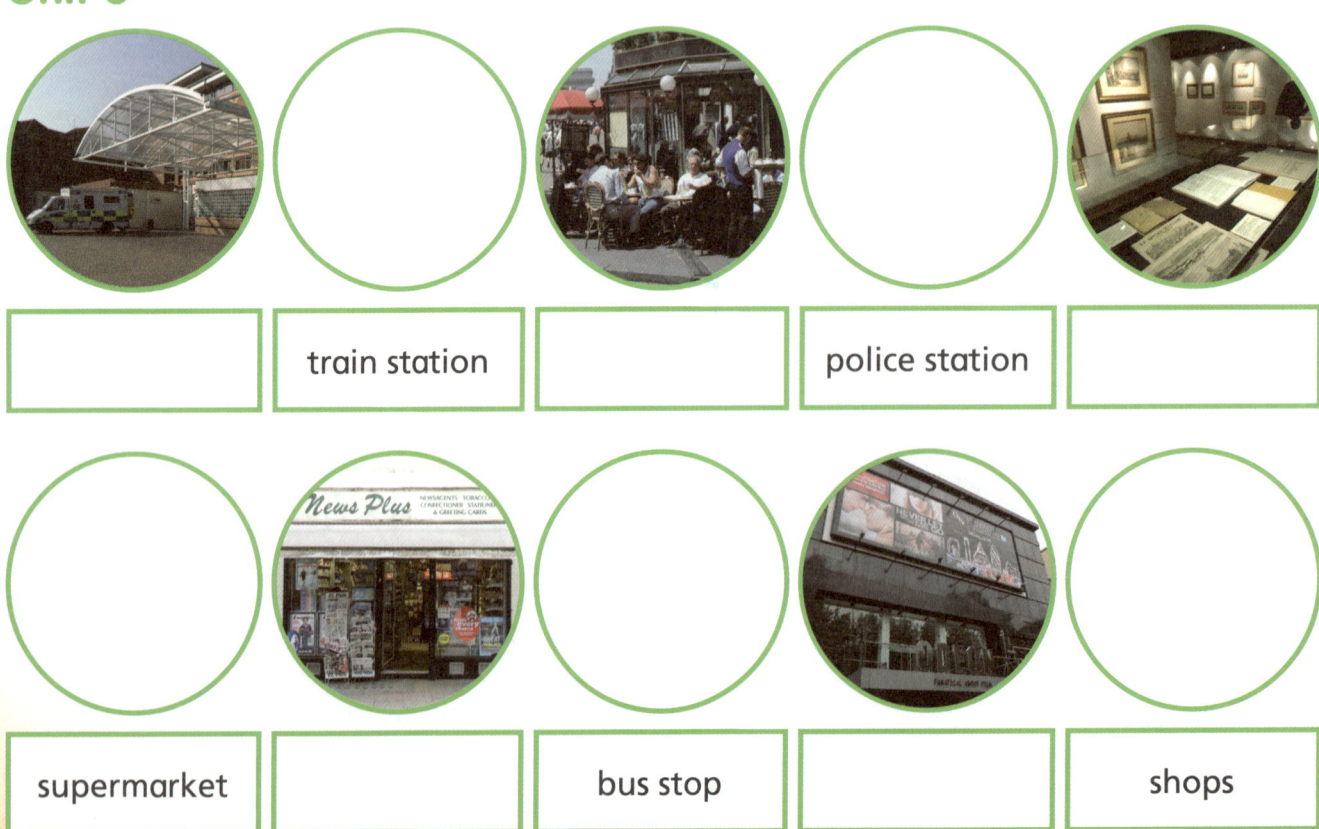

	train station		police station	

supermarket		bus stop		shops

Unit 4

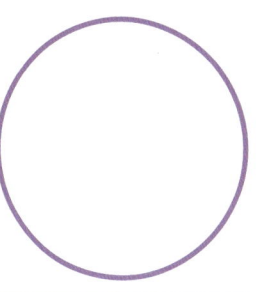

| | police officer | | firefighter | |

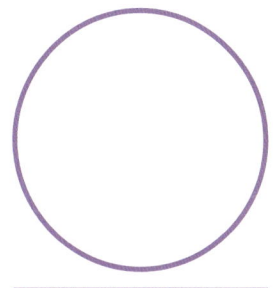

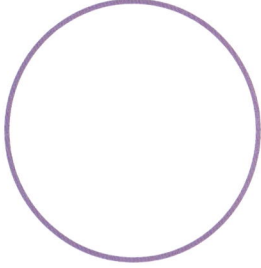

| taxi driver | | pop star | | web designer |

Unit 5

| | collecting stickers | | talking to friends | |

| painting pictures | | using the computer | | shopping |

Picture Dictionary

	river		forest	

bridge		signpost		campsite

Unit 7

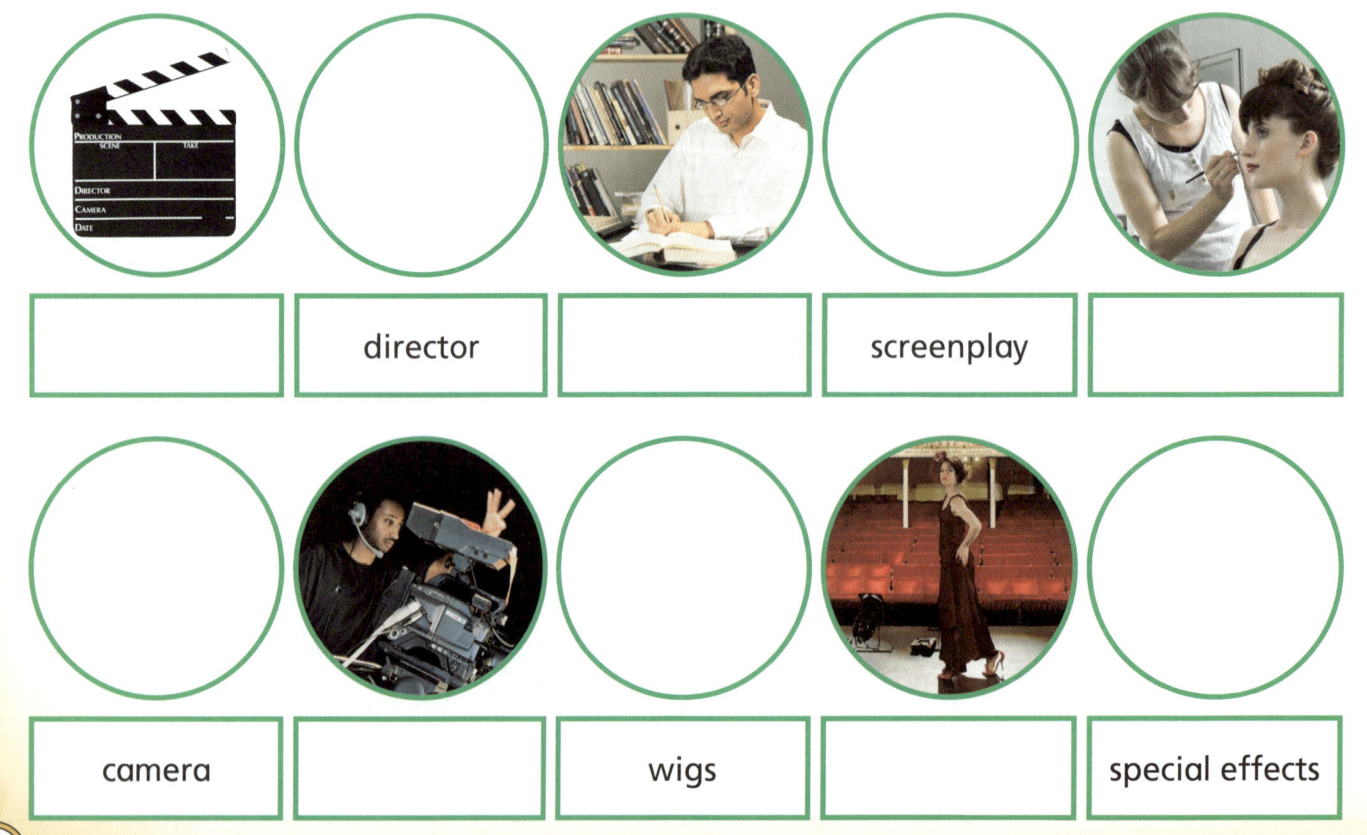

	director		screenplay	

camera		wigs		special effects

Grammar Reference Bank

Unit 1 *Have got* to talk about your school timetable

Grammar presentation

- After **I**, **you**, **we** and **they**, we use **have**.
- After **he** and **she**, we use **has**.
- We put **Have** and **Has** first to make a question.
- We use **short answers** to reply to questions.

Remember!
No got in the short answer!

I You We They	have got	PE. maths. art and design. English.
He She	has got	ICT. geography.

I You We They	haven't got	geography. history. music. science. drama. maths.
He She	hasn't got	

Have	I you we they	got	history today?
Has	he she		

Yes, No,	I you we they	have. haven't.
	he she	has. hasn't.

Grammar check

1 Write sentences to mean the opposite.

1 She has got music today. *She hasn't got music today.*
2 They haven't got maths. _____
3 I have got art and design. _____
4 He hasn't got ICT. _____

2 Complete the questions. Write answers.

1 *Have* they got English today? No, *they haven't* .
2 _____ she got science today? No, _____.
3 _____ you got drama today? Yes, _____.

Grammar self-assessment

Look and colour.

I don't understand anything.	I understand a little.	I understand a lot.	I understand everything.

Unit 2 *Has got* to describe people

Grammar presentation

- We use **has got** for **he** and **she**.
- We use **have got** for **I, you, we** and **they**.
- We put **Has** or **Have** first to make a question.

**Remember!
No got in the short answer!**

I You We They	have got	fair hair. straight hair. long hair. dark hair. a beard. a ponytail.
He She	has got	

I You We They	haven't got	dark hair. curly hair. short hair. long hair. a moustache. glasses.
He She	hasn't got	

Have	I you we they	got	a beard?
Has	she he		a moustache?

Yes, No,	I you we they	have. haven't.
	he she	has. hasn't.

Grammar check

1 **Look and write *He* or *She*.**

1 _____ hasn't got long hair.   2 _____ hasn't got glasses.

3 _____ has got glasses.   4 _____ has got a moustache.

2 **Order and write. Then answer.**

 1 got / Have / they / glasses / ?
Have they got glasses?
No, they haven't.

 2 beard / ? / Has / a / got / he
_____
_____

 3 curly / she / Has / got / hair / ?
_____
_____

 4 they / dark / Have / got / hair / ? / long
_____
_____

Grammar self-assessment

Look and colour.

| I don't understand anything. | I understand a little. | I understand a lot. | I understand everything. |

Unit 3 *There is / there are* to talk about buildings in a town

Grammar presentation

- For singular objects, we use **there is** + **a**.
- For plural objects, we use **there are** + **some / many / lots of**.

Remember!
there's = there is!

There's	a	café	in my street / town / city.
There isn't		park	

Is there a cinema?	Yes, there is.
	No, there isn't.

There are	some many lots of	houses shops cafés	in my street / town / city.
There aren't	any		

Are there any shops?	Yes, there are.
	No, there aren't.

Grammar check

1 **Order and write. Circle *T* (True) or *F* (False).**

1 a / cinema / in / street / the / There's   <u>There's a cinema in the street.</u> (T)/ F

2 four / There / are / in / cafés / street / the   _____   T / F

3 any / There / museums / aren't   _____   T / F

4 stop / a / There / isn't / bus   _____   T / F

5 lots / are / There / of / houses   _____   T / F

2 **Complete the questions. Look at Activity 1 and write the answers.**

1 __Is__ there a supermarket?   <u>No,</u>

2 _____ there any shops?   <u>Yes,</u>

3 _____ there a sweet shop?   _____

4 _____ there any museums?   _____

5 _____ there a bus stop?   _____

Grammar self-assessment

Look and colour.

| I don't understand anything. | I understand a little. | I understand a lot. | I understand everything. |

Unit 4 Present simple 3ʳᵈ person *s* to talk about what people do

Grammar presentation

- We add **s** to the verb to make affirmative sentences for **he** and **she**.
- We use **Does** to make a yes / no question.
- We use **doesn't** to make negative sentences.

Remember!
Affirmative, negative or question, there is always an **s** somewhere.

He	works	on a farm.
She	wears	a uniform.

He	doesn't work	in a hospital.
She	doesn't drive	a car.

Does he	work	with animals?
Does she	wear	a uniform?

Yes, he does.
No, she doesn't.

Grammar check

1 Look and complete the questions. Write the answers.

1 __Does__ he wear a uniform?   Yes, he does.

Does _____ drive a car?   _____

_____ he work in a hospital?   _____

2 Does she wear a uniform____   _____

Does _____ work with people?   _____

_____ she work in a library?   _____

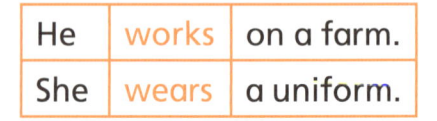

2 Look, read and circle. Act out.

1 Does (he) / she work with a computer?

2 Yes, he do / does. He work / works with a computer every day.

3 Does he wear / wears a uniform?

4 No, he does / doesn't, but he designs / design uniforms.

5 Is / Does he a fashion designer?

6 Yes, he is / does.

Grammar self-assessment

Look and colour.

I don't understand anything.	I understand a little.	I understand a lot.	I understand everything.

Unit 5 *Like + ing* to talk about activities we like doing

Grammar presentation

- We add **ing** to verbs after **like**.
- We use **Do** or **Does** to make yes / no questions.

Remember!
We also add **ing** to the verb after **prefer** and **love**.

I You We They	(don't) like	play**ing** football. us**ing** the computer.

Do	I you we they	like	shopp**ing**?

He She	likes	rollerskat**ing**.
	doesn't like	danc**ing**.

Does	he she	like	paint**ing** pictures?

Grammar check

1 Read and circle. Act out.

1 What (**do**) / **does** you like doing at the weekends?

2 I like **talk** / **talking** to my friends.

3 **Do** / **Does** you like **dancing** / **dance**?

4 No, I **don't** / **do**. I **likes** / **like** watching films on DVD.

5 Do you **like** / **likes** rollerskating?

6 No, I don't. I **prefer** / **prefers** ice skating.

2 Order and write.

1 likes / Ellie / the / using / computer   *Ellie likes using the computer.*

2 stickers / collecting / loves / Nasim   _____

3 pictures / Clare / like / painting / Does / ?   _____

4 to / Oliver / listening / music / likes   _____

5 Ben / like / shopping / doesn't   _____

Grammar self-assessment

Look and colour.

I don't understand anything.	I understand a little.	I understand a lot.	I understand everything.

Unit 6 Imperatives for giving instructions and directions

Grammar presentation

- We use the verb without a subject to give instructions.
- We put **Don't** in front of the verb to give a negative instruction.

> **Remember!**
> You can give instructions to one person or a lot of people, but the verb doesn't change.

Turn	left at the tree.
Go	over the bridge.
Remember	to close the gate.

Don't	turn	right at the tree.
Don't	go	round the farm.
Don't	forget	to close the gate.

Grammar check

1 **Look and write.**

~~Don't~~ Don't ~~turn~~ Turn Go Go Go go ~~right~~ right over
straight round the the the bridge over at

1 *Don't turn right.*
2 _____ the bridge.
3 _____ on.
4 _____ lake.
5 _____
6 _____ tree.

2 **Look, read and match.**

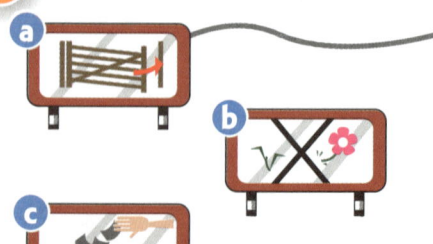

1 Close the gate.
2 Don't cut down trees.
3 Don't drop litter.
4 Put your litter in a bin.
5 Don't pick flowers.
6 Don't light fires.

Grammar self-assessment

Look and colour.

| I don't understand anything. | I understand a little. | I understand a lot. | I understand everything. |

Unit 7 *Tiger Street Club* Revision Game

1 **Play the game with a friend.**

HELLO

Start here!

1 Ask a friend their name, age and where they live.

2 Ask a friend what they like doing at the weekend.

3 Describe your school.

4 Say when you have got English lessons.

5 Go forward one square!

6 Ask a friend when their birthday is.

7 Describe someone in the classroom.

8 Describe a job.

9 Say how you go to school.

10 Go back one square!

11 Describe your village / town / city.

12 Say what types of books you like reading.

13 Give directions to the school canteen.

14 Say what animals and plants live in or grow on trees.

15 Say what you do after school.

Finish

25x5=125

2 **Colour the squares of the game to show what you can do.**

Green = I can do this well.   Orange = I can do this.   Red = I need more practice.

Reading Extension

 **Tiger Team**

1 Read.

DINOSAURS IN MUSEUMS!

There aren't any dinosaurs alive today. So how do we know what they look like? Well, there are museums about dinosaurs all around the world. The museums show us dinosaur bones, eggs and teeth! There are lots of models of dinosaurs, too. Some of them are huge!

At the Natural History Museum in London, in the UK, there is a model of a Tyrannosaurus Rex. It moves and roars like a real dinosaur. Its teeth are 15 centimetres long. You can also see a model of baby Maiasaura dinosaurs hatching from their eggs. There are 20 to 30 eggs in the nest. Each egg is about the same size as an ostrich egg!

This museum in Indianapolis, in the USA, has got giant models of dinosaurs on the outside. A small dinosaur is climbing through the window and a big one is looking inside!

At some museums, you can also see models of dinosaur footprints in the ground. These can be very small, but most of them are much bigger than our feet. Some are bigger than our bodies!

Do YOU know...?
The word 'dinosaur' means 'great lizard'.

Magazine

Our Amazing World

2 **Look and write.**

bone   teeth   model   roar   ~~hatch~~   ostrich   footprint   huge

      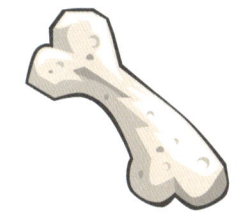   

1 _hatch_   2 _____   3 _____   4 _____

5 _____   6 _____   7 _____   8 _____

3 **Read and write. You can use 1, 2 or 3 words.**

1 Most dinosaur footprints are much _____bigger_____ than our feet.

2 There _____ any dinosaurs alive today.

3 Three things that you can find in dinosaur museums are dinosaur _____, _____ and _____.

4 Some models of dinosaurs are _____.

5 A Maiasaura egg and an _____ egg are about the same size.

 **Personalisation**

4 **Read, write and draw.**

1 My favourite dinosaur is the _____.

2 It's (*big, dangerous*) _____.

3 It's got _____.

4 It can _____.

5 It eats _____.

Tiger Team

1 Read.

Brilliant buildings!

People live and work in many different kinds of buildings. Let's look at some of them.

This building in London, in the UK, is called The Shard. It's taller than any other building in Western Europe. It has got glass on all four sides. Inside the building, there are offices, homes and restaurants. You can go to the top and see the whole of London!

This house in Canada has got a lot of glass, too. The building is made of glass bottles. The walls are made of green and brown bottles and cement. The tables and chairs inside the house are made of bottles, too.

This building is a hotel. People come here on holiday. There aren't any roads, so people travel by cable car across the mountains. The building isn't made of bricks or cement. It's made of ice! It's called the Ice Hotel and it's in Romania.

Some buildings have got bright colours or pictures on the outside. Sometimes, the colours and pictures help us to know what the building is. Look at this imaginative building in Kansas, in the USA. What do you think it is?

Yes, it's a library! The walls look like shelves full of enormous books.

Do YOU know...?

The Gate Tower building in Japan has got a busy road going through the middle of it!

Magazine Our Amazing World

2 Read and match.

1 There aren't any roads …   green and brown bottles.
2 There are offices, homes and restaurants …   inside and outside the building.
3 The glass bottle house building is made of …   isn't made of bricks or cement.
4 The Kansas City Library has got books …   near the Ice Hotel.
5 The Ice Hotel in Romania …   inside The Shard.

3 Look and read. Write *True* or *False*.

1 There are four brown bottles on the table outside the restaurant.   *False*

2 There is snow on the mountains.   _____

3 The cable car is blue and green.   _____

4 The hotel is between the restaurant and the library.   _____

5 The man climbing the ladder is wearing a red jacket.   _____

6 There aren't any cars on the road.   _____

Personalisation

4 Read, write and draw.

1 My favourite building is _____.

2 Where is it? _____

3 On the outside, it's (*tall, colourful*) _____
_____.

4 What's inside? _____

5 What's it made of? _____

Tiger Team

Wonderful plants

1 Read.

Plants are all around us. Most of us see grass, trees and flowers every day. Some plants grow delicious fruit and vegetables, too. Plants around the world are very different. Different plants like different environments. Some places are very hot, some places are cold, some are dry, and some are very wet.

Plants need water, but the desert is hot and dry. Can plants live in the desert? Yes, they can. Cactus plants can live in the desert. They store rainwater inside. They can live without water for many weeks.

Some plants catch insects for food. This plant is a Venus flytrap. It attracts insects with a sweet nectar and when they land on the plant, the leaves close. Then, the plant eats the insect!

Look at this giant redwood tree. It's so big that this woman is standing inside the trunk. These are the tallest trees in the world. They can be 90 metres tall!

Water lilies live in rivers and lakes. They have got roots at the bottom of the river or lake, and they have got round leaves that stay on top of the water. These giant water lilies in Brazil have got very big leaves. Some are three metres wide. That's the size of a small boat!

Do YOU know...?

Giant redwoods can live for a long time, more than 2000 years!

Magazine

Our Amazing World

2 Find and circle. Look and write.

1 _roots_

2 _____

3 _____

4 _____

5 _____

6 _____

7 _____

8 _____

3 Read and write. You can use 1, 2 or 3 words.

1 Cactus plants live in the ___desert___. There _____ much water there.

2 Water lilies have got leaves _____ of the water, and roots _____ of the river or lake.

3 A Venus flytrap eats _____.

4 Some tree trunks are so big that people can _____ inside them.

Personalisation

4 Read, write and draw.

1 My favourite plant is _____.

2 It grows in _____.

3 I like it because _____.

4 My favourite plants to eat are _____
_____.

Tiger Team

An Amazing Book: Peter Pan

1 Read.

Peter Pan is a book by a Scottish writer called J M Barrie.

The story is about a boy called Peter Pan. He lives in Neverland. He's a special boy – he can fly and he doesn't grow up. One day, he visits three children in their house in London. They are called Wendy, John and Michael. They all travel together to Neverland and have lots of adventures.

Peter Pan has got an enemy called Captain Hook. He's a pirate and he wants to catch Peter Pan. But Captain Hook is also scared of a crocodile. The children all work together and win. Then, the crocodile catches and eats Captain Hook!

Many films have been made about Peter Pan, too. In this cartoon, Peter Pan is wearing a green shirt and a green hat with a red feather. People can watch the films in the cinema or on DVD.

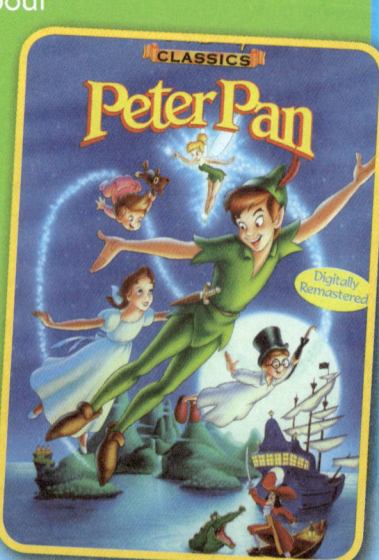

People can also see the story of Peter Pan at the theatre. There is sometimes music and dancing. The actors in the theatre look like they can fly through the air! Special clothes and equipment help create the special effects.

Do YOU know...?
The story of Peter Pan is more than 100 years old!

Magazine > Our Amazing World

2 **Read and write.**

enemy   crocodile   adventures   cinema   Michael   ~~fly~~

1 Peter Pan is special because he can _____ *fly* _____.

2 John and _____ are brothers.

3 The children have lots of _____ in Neverland.

4 Captain Hook is an _____ of Peter Pan.

5 At the end, the _____ eats Captain Hook.

6 You can see Peter Pan at the _____, on DVD or at the theatre.

3 **Look and read. Write *True* or *False*.**

1 Two children on the stage are holding hands.   *True*

2 Two people are flying.   _____

3 Peter Pan has got a feather in his hat.   _____

4 A woman is playing the violin.   _____

5 The audience is scared.   _____

6 Captain Hook has got long, dark hair.   _____

Personalisation

4 **Read, write and draw.**

1 Who is your favourite character from a story?

_____

2 Why do you like the character? _____

_____

3 Is the character from a book, a film or the theatre?

_____

4 What's the character's story about?

_____

_____

_____

Speaking Extension

Speaking Extension 1

Find the differences.

Look at these pictures. They look the same, but some things are different. In picture 1, there is a picture of a train on the wall. In picture 2, there is a picture of a bus. Can you spot nine more differences?

Tell the story.

These pictures show a story. Look at the pictures and say what happens next.

1. *Eddie is outside. He's reading. It's sunny and he's very hot.*

Look at the pictures. Which is the odd one out? Say why.

You will see sets of four pictures. You must say which picture is the odd one out in each set and explain why. Look at the example to help you.

1. *Picture c is the odd one out because Brazil isn't in Europe.*

Find the differences.

Look at these pictures. They look the same, but some things are different.
In picture 1, the dog has got long ears. In picture 2, the dog has got short ears.
Can you spot nine more differences?

Tell the story.

These pictures show a story. Look at the pictures and say what happens next.

1. *Anna is playing with her cat. They're playing with a ball. It's fun.*

Look at the pictures. Which is the odd one out? Say why.

You will see sets of four pictures. You must say which picture is the odd one out in each set and explain why. Look at the example to help you.

1. *Picture d is the odd one out because he isn't doing a job.*

Speaking Extension 7

Tell the story.

These pictures show a story. Look at the pictures and say what happens next.

1. *Emma and her family are going camping. They're all in the car. Emma is very excited.*

January	February	March
April	May	June
July	August	September
October	November	December

9:00	9:15	9:30	10:00	10:45

  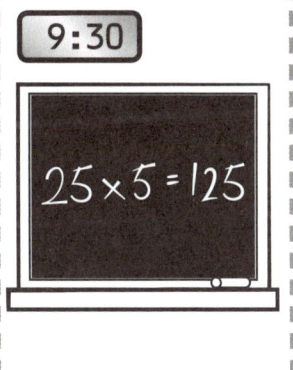  

11:00	11:30	1:00	2:15	2:45

   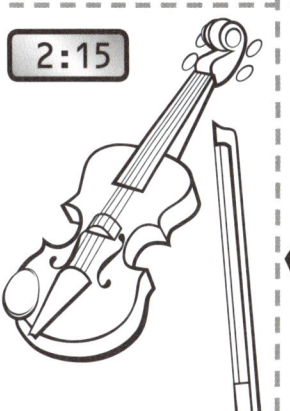 

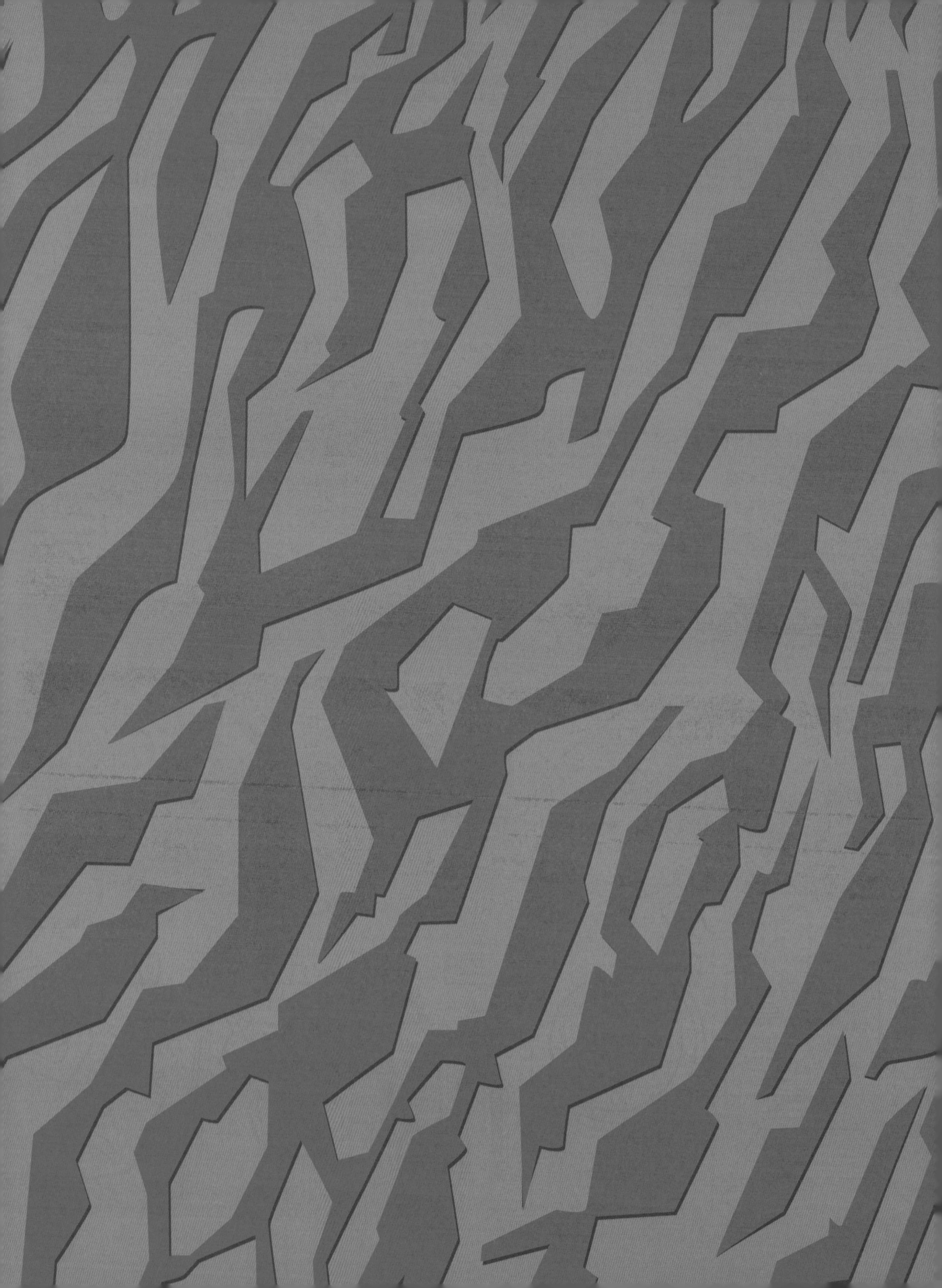

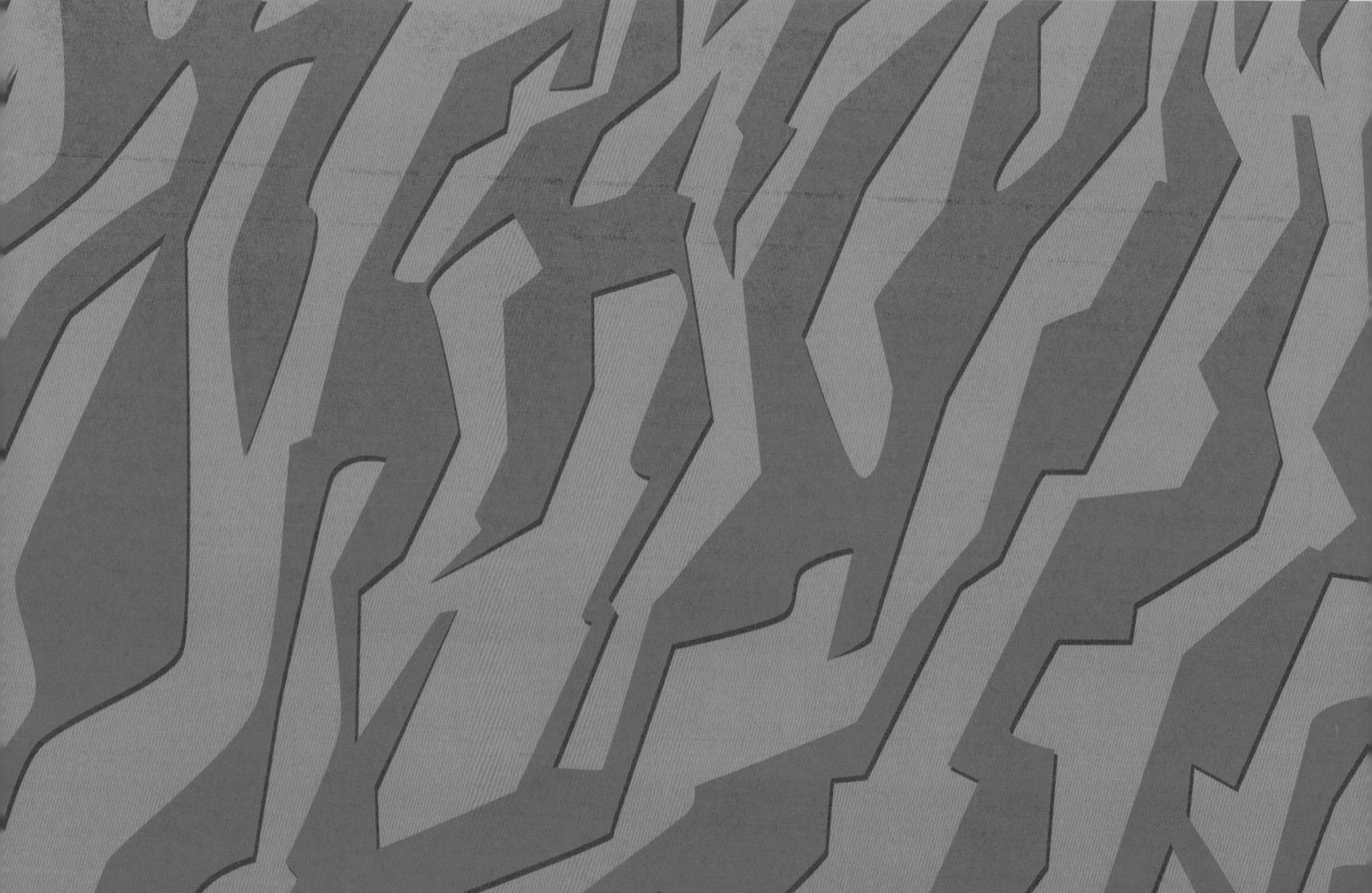

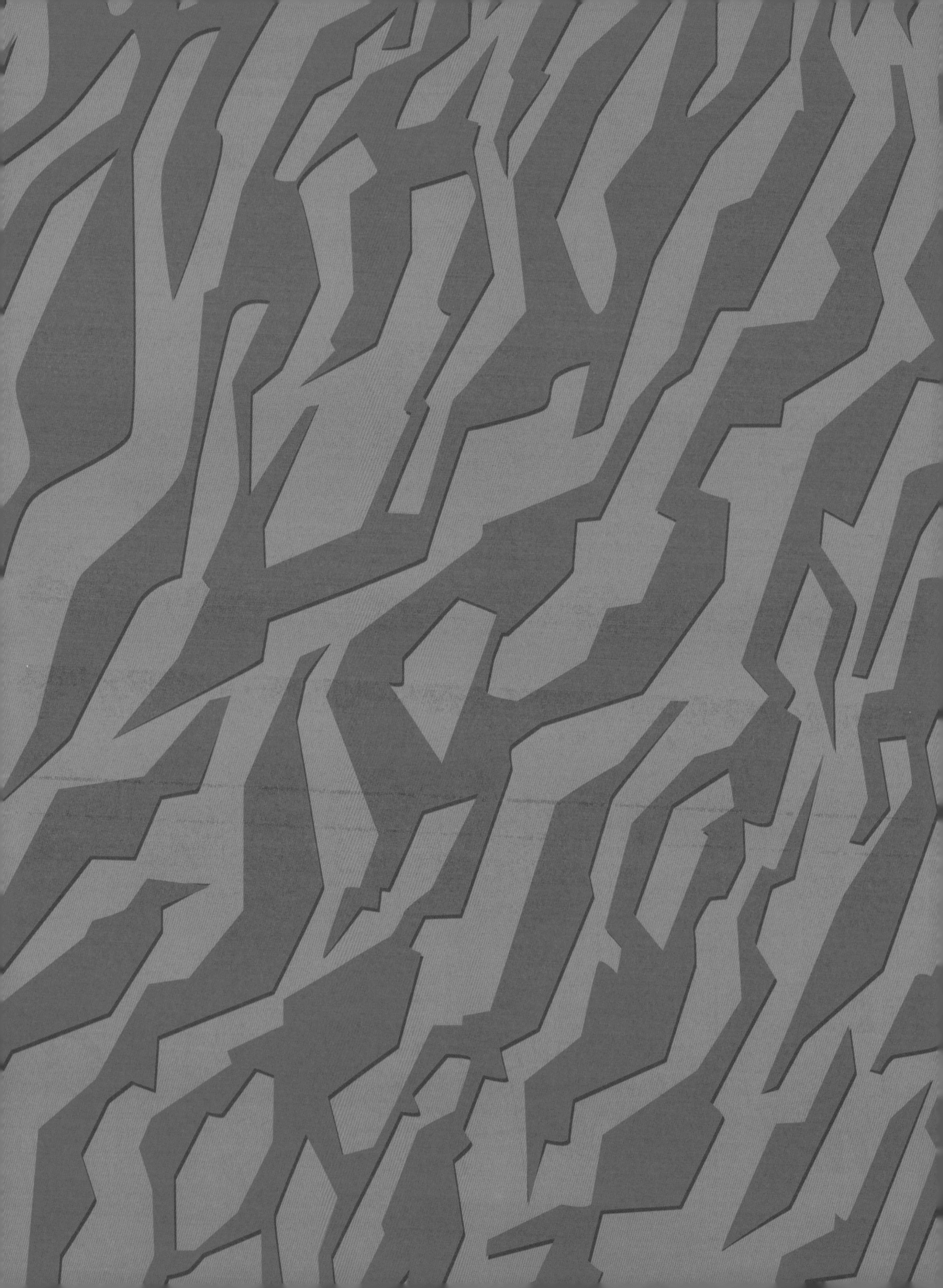

Go over the bridge.

Don't go straight on.

Don't go under the bridge.

Go to the campsite.

Go straight on.

Go round the forest and turn left at the signpost.

Go round the lake and turn right at the farm.

Go to the end of the path and then turn left.

Don't turn left. Turn right.

Turn right at the end of the road.

We've got geography in the gym with Julie.

A ghost under a signpost says, 'Don't go over the bridge'.

Victor the vet drives a very dirty van.

A dog on a rock says, 'Do not get lost in the forest'.

Frank the firefighter fights the flames.

Where's Sarah? She's over there. She's got fair hair.

Princess Lynne likes playing the violin in her room.

Here's Pierce. He's got a long beard. And he's got big ears.

There are six supermarkets and seven cinemas in the city centre.

There's a museum and a newsagent's opposite the zoo.

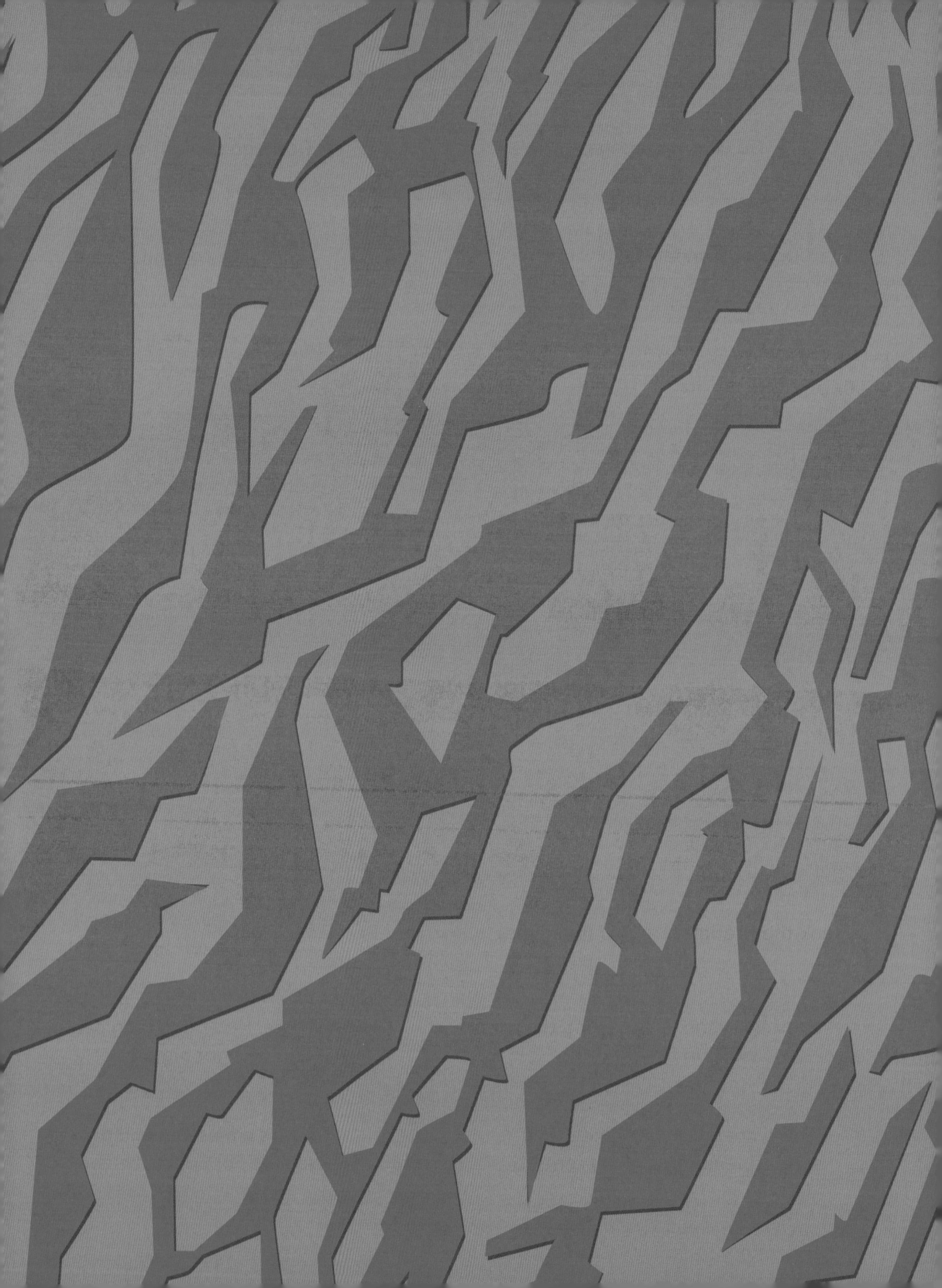

| ten | thirty | fifty | seventy | ninety |

| English | maths | PE | geography | music |

| curly hair | beard | dark hair | long hair | moustache |

| hospital | café | museum | newsagent's | cinema |

Unit 4

farmer

nurse

fashion designer

vet

shop assistant

Unit 5

reading comics

taking photos

going to museums

rollerskating

dancing

Unit 6

mountain

lake

path

gate

farm

Unit 7

clapperboard

writer

make-up artist

cameraman

actress